D0380878

Greg Stier
with Jane Dratz

D2S Publishing

D2S Publishing

Firestarter
Copyright © 2010 by Dare 2 Share Ministries, Inc.
All rights reserved.

A D2S Publishing book
PO Box 745323
Arvada, CO 80006

This is a work of fiction. With the exception of known historical
characters, all characters are the product of the author's
imagination.

Stier, Greg and Dratz, Jane.
Firestarter: Fuel Your Passion
ISBN-13: 978-0-9725507-6-5
Library of Congress Control Number: 2009907126

Printed in the United States of America

To teenagers everywhere.
May you unleash THE Cause and
change the world through Jesus,
one life at a time.

My Scion peeled out of the Denny's parking lot. I could hardly believe Jen and I had totally missed the Friday night party scene. What was up with my friends tonight, anyway?

I guess when you think about it, the past few hours of conversation were actually pretty intense. What started as a jaunt to up our caffeine levels at Starbucks this afternoon had taken a weird left turn into the topic of Jesus and my friend Nick's idea of what being a Christian is really about. Then the outing to Denny's after seeing Kailey in *Grease* had detoured once again into some seriously deep

FIRESTARTER

stuff. Instead of heading to the after-party, our tight foursome spent an hour over our late dinner/early breakfast of Grand Slams talking about the purpose of life, God and relationships.

So at the end of the day, thanks to Nick, my friend and favorite party girl, Jen, with her flashing blue eyes and long blond hair, had supposedly gone from a quasi-Catholic/agnostic something-or-other to a "Venti" Christian—our new code name for a "seriously intense" follower of Jesus. And Kailey, our talented, popular, high-energy, reigning drama queen, was now seriously intrigued by a relationship with Jesus too. Me? I'd gone from a self-assured atheist to a questioning one.

I'd shut down my long-time friend Nick too many times to remember over the past four years, whenever he even hinted about religion talk. But today had been different. Jen had been snagged by nice-sounding and (to my thinking) pretty simplistic words, while Kailey and I had agreed to read some part of the Bible called "John," mostly to make Nick and Jen happy. What's the harm—I'd read some Greek philosophy in English class junior year. Those books didn't change my life one bit.

CHAPTER 1

One thing I do understand now is why Nick calls his thing with Jesus "a relationship with God and not a religion." Religion's something I've never wanted to get roped into, but a relationship with God, that's a whole new idea to me.

Whatever.

Sure, Nick definitely caught my attention and started me thinking about new possibilities, but now, as I accelerate down the street in my brand new Scion, I'm settling back into my comfort zone. My big mistake was that I promised him I'd read his little book of John. But I can assure you there won't be any miracles. I said I'd read it tonight. Where was I when that happened? Stupid intense moment.

By the way, I'm Jared, second semester senior jock at Brentwood High School. Tall, handsome, smart, if I say so myself, and headed to state college on a full track scholarship. Also, I'm not embarrassed to tell you up front that Jen and I have just recently started to develop a little special chemistry. Both of us are still stepping cautiously around the edges of a romantic involvement, but believe me, a guy knows when a girl is interested. Still, all that was before all this Jesus stuff hit. Not sure how Jen's "God moment" will play out in her social life. I'm sure she's still a party girl at heart. You can't just switch that off.

Anyway, I wonder if Jen bought into all this religious stuff because of her crappy home life. To be honest, all the members of our Four Musketeers crew have parents with "issues." Jen has an alcoholic, abusive Dad. Nick, the straight-up Christian, has a Mom who sleeps around. Imagine that. Kailey has a controlling, manipulative Mom. And me, well, I have to deal with my demanding, perfectionist father who's made it very, very clear to me that I'll never measure up. All four of us swear we'll never be anything like our parents.

All for one, and one for all.

Kailey's Journal

March 22nd

HOLY CRAP, it's 1:00 AM and I still can't sleep. There's too much craziness going through my head from tonight. Maybe if I write some of it down it won't all feel like it needs to run through my head at the same time.

1) Grease was awesome! woo-hoo! I can't believe it actually happened. The audience absolutely loved me as Sandy And the escape plan is in motion! I've got my full ride drama scholarship to Arizona state.

Mom's finely manicured claws are about to lose their control on my life! She loves to flash her fake, botoxed smile whenever her domination is imposed. Just last weekend, I waited until she stopped giggling and the newest boy toy had crept out the front door (wow, she's sooooo sneaky), before going down to grab breakfast and head out the door for

Blah ⋆ College money ⋆ Blah
Blah ⋆ Blah You are *so* lucky!
⋆ Blah ⋆

some reason, she started jabbering on about
college (no one knows how the plastic mind
behind that plastic face operates). she lectured
me about how lucky I was that Dad was paying
for college and how I had so many choices &
opportunities. what she didn't remind me of was
the catch (there is ~~usually~~ ALWAYS a catch
with her). I only get the cash from Dad if I go
to school within a hundred miles of her pretty
little claws (I think that distance was part of
the Divorce settlement). we only talked about
this "minor" detail once, and since all the
college app deadlines are past, she thinks
she's in the clear. what she didn't know is
that I applied to Arizona State (323 beautiful
miles away). And now her plans for "lifelong
kailey domination" are devastated. I've earned
my own way off this 100 mile leash. YES!!!

while I'm excited, I'm also a little ~~nervous~~
scared...what if I get to Asu and I'm still not
happy with my life? I've always told my friends
that Mom is the reason I'm not happy with my
life, but what if she's not the only reason?
what if there's something inside me that will
never be satisfied?? Even the bright lights

and my <u>standing-o</u> tonight at Grease didn't quite
fill up that space deep down inside me...it just
feels like there's something still missing...I'm
longing for something, and don't quite know
what...

I'm glad Nick, Jared, Jen & I ended up at Denny's
instead of the after-party tonight. They caught
me up on the conversation they had about
religion and God at Starbucks before the play
(Jen bought into the Jesus thing — yeah, who
would have thought...) and then we started in on
one of our own. Nick really seems to know what
he's talking about.

For some reason I can't get the cancer thing out
of my head. Tonight Nick compared cancer to sin
and how both of them eat away at you. Maybe
because Pappy died of cancer just about this
time last year. Dang, if I'd had a cure for that,
I would have done anything...And what if sin
really is like cancer? It makes some sense.
There is something inside me that doesn't quite
feel healthy. A nagging self-doubt that no
matter how hard I try and what I do, things
won't work out and, worse, nothing will actually
matter. There's something missing in me.
Something important. The whole cancer/sin talk

tonight felt like it poured salt into that wound and it's been nagging at me ever since we left Denny's. I really hope there is a cure for this emptiness...

Dang it. Still don't feel like sleep.

um...well I'm supposed to read the book of John in the Bible and supposedly that has something to do with the cure to sin cancer. Might as well start now, nothing better to do with my insomnia. Though who knows how much I'll remember in the morning? I better jot myself some notes about it. There's a Bible around here somewhere, that one Pappy gave me.

okay, here we go —

(Later) I'm surprised at how interesting and enticing this book is. I'm through the first four chapters and it's not dry & boring like I thought it'd be. Yeah, there's definitely stuff here that doesn't really make sense to me ("the word was God and the word was with God...") but I can tell you one thing, it ain't boring! oh and something else I've figured out — Jesus was no meek & mild wimp! By

Chapter 2, he's running people out of the
temple with a whip! Though He's not always
like that either – in chapter 3, this religious
guy, Nico-something, comes to Jesus late at
night (hiding something, eh?) and he seems
super scared and Jesus responds by being
really loving. Jesus tells Nico that he just
has to believe and he gets eternal life. Wow,
is it really that simple???

I really liked chapter 4, it resonated with me.
It's Jesus & this lady at a well talking about
water and her life. She seemed to freak out
that Jesus was even talking to her, and having
read a little about this dude, I sorta agree with
her. Then he offered her "living water" so she
wouldn't be thirsty again. But I don't think he
was talking about physical thirst, but some
deeper thirst. Hmm... I was writing earlier
about how it feels like something is missing
inside me right now and how nothing really
seems fulfilling. Maybe this "living water" is
what I need. I've been trying to make myself
happy through relationships, track, acting. None
of them seem to work. That woman tried hard
to find satisfaction too (with five ex-husbands to
show for it), but nothing worked.

Living H2O

Then she met Jesus and everything changed. He filled that deep thirst inside her. Could the same thing quench my thirst? Does it really work like that? Or is Jesus just about a bunch of rules like, "Do this/Don't do that"? The last thing I want to do is replace my mom's control with a bunch of Christian rules. But this woman at the well certainly didn't seem to think Jesus was all about rules. I really hope that's true. Okay, time to read some more.

(Later) Wow, that went fast. I finished it! Mom would kill me if she knew I was up this late. Too bad. This is all far too exciting! There's so much that sticks out! The part that really struck me is when they kill him. After all the people Jesus healed & helped, after all the great advice he gave, everyone around him just walks away. The religious guys lie about him, his friends slink away and the men guarding him torture and kill him. Talk about being let down & betrayed. How could they do that to him? They said this guy was God.

If I'd been Jesus, lightning bolts would suddenly have become very important parts of all those guys' lives and deaths. But he didn't

Do that. Maybe that's what real love is. And Jesus is sooo forgiving, like with the woman the religious guys were going to stone. ("I don't condemn you either.") There's something really different and...intriguing...about him.

He's S☀forgiving!

And what was it Nick said tonight? That Jesus was crucified for me. That he took all the false accusations, betrayals, beatings and death for me. It's like I can feel him looking me in the eye saying, "I'm doing this for you." Dang, that gives me the chills. So why'd he do it? Well from what I've read & heard tonight, it's about curing that spiritual cancer and giving me eternal life. It's liberating and not about rules at all – it's about love. He did it for me. Wow. I still can't quite get my mind around that. He loves me sooo much! How could I say "no" to that? How could anyone say "no" to that?

Yeah, I believe that. Just writing this has made me feel so much more relaxed, like the pieces in me are getting put back together. Let's see if I can pull off this whole prayer thing.

Dear GOD,

I really Don't exactly know what to say, but I know that you love me and I want to thank you for that. I know that I mess up a lot and I believe what Nick was telling me: that there's nothing I can Do to fix myself. But you can, GOD. And I want you to. Thank you for what you Did for me. I can't imagine anyone else giving their life for me, and you're GOD! you are AMAZING! I had no idea you were the thing that was missing from my life. I trust in you to forgive me for all my sins and give me that thing you talked about in the book of John called "eternal life." The way I feel now makes me want to tell everyone I know about you!

Thank you for loving me & forgiving me.
I love you!

kailey

2

I woke up to find a text from Kailey, "I just became a Christian. Do u hate me?"

I should have seen this coming. Heck, I practically set up a first date between her and Jesus last night at Denny's. I was totally expecting that popular, talented Kailey would shut Nick and Jen down when they brought up all the God stuff. But hey, to each his own. I'm open-minded.

So, I texted her back, "Of course I hate u. Have u told Jen and Nick yet?"

FIRESTARTER

The message came back, "About 2."

I sent back, "LMK what happens."

As I sat in my room waiting for Kailey to get back to me, I noticed the little book of John lying on my desk, staring up at me accusingly. I know I promised Nick I'd read it, but not now. I'm just not in the mood to be brainwashed. I don't want to deal with some mystical, mood-enhancing, bearded 2,000-year-old holy man who is capturing the imagination of all my best friends. Who'd a thought? Kailey, too? I have better things to do. There are a couple YouTube videos that have been calling to me.

My cell phone ring interrupted the second one. Something big must've happened for Kailey to call instead of text me back. Confident it was her, I flipped it open and asked, "So, what'd they say?"

"Who are *they*?" asked the male voice on the other end of the phone.

"Ahhh…Nick?" I asked.

"Who were you expecting?" he responded.

CHAPTER 2

"What's up, dude?" I asked, ignoring his question.

"I want to ask you a favor, Jared," he said with Nick-like sincerity.

"Shoot."

With a quiver of nervousness in his voice he launched into his request. "Just got off the phone with Kailey and Jen and they're coming to church with me tomorrow. Uhh…we want you to come with us. What d'ya think?"

"I don't know, Nick. Seriously, dude, do you really think that—"

He cut me off with the words, "—all for one, and one for all."

This Jesus stuff is starting to get seriously out of control. But all my friends seem headed down this road. I should probably keep tabs on them and make sure they haven't bitten off more than they can chew. Anyway, it might be kind of entertaining, though it'll be hard to keep my opinions to myself—then again if I don't, I might get lynched. Besides, I always say I'm open to new experiences.

"Okay, I'll go. Do I have to go buy a suit or something like that?"

Nick laughed. "No. Just come as you are."

"Well, right now I'm in my SpongeBob Squarepants boxers and a t-shirt."

He laughed again. "Maybe throw a pair of pants on." He told me he'd pick me up at 9:15. I told him I'd meet him there instead, just in case I had to make a fast getaway.

Hanging up the phone, I pictured myself, the infamous atheist, in an actual church service. I imagined villagers with torches and pitchforks chasing the Frankenstein atheist out of a cathedral. Realizing the ridiculousness of my what-will-church-be-like assessment, I reined in my "religion is the opiate of the masses" imagery and shifted my thoughts to pipe organs and stained glass. Boring. Oh well, at least it beat pitchforks.

What have I gotten myself into?

Walking into the church from the parking lot, I was a little encouraged. The people looked surprisingly normal. No lynch mobs here. Nobody waiting at the door to give me grape Kool-Aid, proclaim "there goeth the heathen!" or ask me for money. I even saw a few people I recognized from school...and they recognized me.

Awkward.

The first thing I noticed when I walked into the lobby was how big the place was and how there were people everywhere. It kind of felt like the lobby surrounding a sports arena, minus the beer vendors and nachos.

In lieu of nachos, smiling people were passing out little program-type things. I took one and flipped through it nervously, trying to look busy and unapproachable. In it was everything I didn't want to know, like details about the upcoming women's meeting and how much money the church raked in last month.

My head jerked up gratefully when I heard my name from across the lobby. It was Nick. As he waved me over, I began to feel regret gurgle up from the pit of my stomach. What was I doing here? All for one, and one for all? Sure, that's good for all the new "converts" in my clique, but suddenly this was beginning to feel like getting my eyelashes plucked one at a time. Clearly, I was feeling conflicted about this whole endeavor. I guess that was a good thing— it meant my logical, rational mind still had a fighting chance. I finally made it over the hot coals to Nick, who held my favorite Frapp in his extended hand.

"Did you stop by Starbucks on the way?" I asked.

"We have a station on the other side of the church," was Nick's response.

"And you didn't get me a Venti Jesus?"

"Oh, that's coming later, after we drench you with holy water," Nick said with a laugh.

I laughed, too…nervously.

"Let's go!" he said, grabbing me by the arm that was decaffeinated.

Soon I heard rock music blaring and saw teens gathering in clusters in front of a room with a sign above the door that said "The Rock." I breathed a sigh of relief.

And what a room it was. To be honest, I was kind of impressed. There were lots of kids, a hundred or so. There were all kinds of posters hanging on the walls and the graphics were pretty cool. They even had a little stage that was decked out with lights, sound monitors, mikes and instruments.

"Jen and Kailey are already here," Nick said, dragging me across the half-filled room.

"I can't believe you actually came!" Jen said with a great big smile on her face as she hugged me.

"I can't either!" both Kailey and I said at exactly the same time.

FIRESTARTER

Looking Kailey square in the eyes, I jettisoned the tact by flat-out asking, "So, you really decided to buy into all this God stuff?"

Expecting a shrug or an embarrassed, mumbled response, instead I got a very sincere, "Yes."

Now I was the one who was a little embarrassed, but I found my footing and said simply, "That's cool, Kailey. If you're happy, then I'm happy. Just don't try to induct me into your Jesus cult."

"Don't worry, Jared, I get the message," she said, "I'm just glad you came."

"All for one—," I started to say before I was interrupted by the piercing sound of feedback from a mike. A twenty-something guy was on the stage trying to quiet the crowd. Instead, everybody squealed their disapproval and covered their ears.

"Oops, sorry about that," the guy said, stepping back from the monitor. "Is that better? Anyway, my name is Eric and I'm the youth pastor here. I wanted to welcome you all to a special edition Sunday service here at The Rock. As a matter of fact, we have a very special guest here with us from Denver, Colorado, who is going to share with us this morning. But before he does, let's worship!"

With that, a band came up and started their Jesus music thing. Everyone seemed to stand on cue as a seventeenish quasi-hot girl began to sing. The crowd started clapping and singing along. Even though the words were projected onto a couple screens, I just stood there with my arms folded, trying to keep my snarl tame while everyone else sang about God being awesome and Jesus dying and great things still to be done in the city and such. It was weird.

After what seemed to be an eternity, the speaker was introduced. I didn't get his name as I was whispering a joke to Nick.

The guy told some kind of funny stories about his "gang member" bodybuilding family becoming Christians. As he did, my eyes vacillated to his sleeves. The guns in those holsters were pea shooters. He must have been at the bottom of DNA barrel or maybe he got a bad batch of steroids in his Christmas stocking. I couldn't help but think that

FIRESTARTER

this guy spent a lot of time locked inside high school lockers growing up. Seemed like a dork to me.

But everyone else thought he was funny, until he got serious.

3

He started talking about "passion fuel," the fuel that drives your life and ignites you into action. He talked about how different people are motivated by different passion fuels when it comes to sharing about Jesus with others. According to the speaker, there were five main fuels and he went through them one by one. I was somewhat intrigued by the topic, wondering if I could figure out which of these motivations had fueled Nick's persistent attempts over the years to talk to me about Jesus.

First, he talked about obedience to God—God told you to, so do it. I knew Nick took the Bible seriously, so initially I figured the first one sounded like a fit for Nick. The speaker used the words "great commission" over and over, saying how Jesus had out-and-out commanded his followers to go tell everyone about how he was the way to God. This made Jesus sound sorta like a drill sergeant to me—kinda like my Dad, actually—which was way different from all the loving, forgiving heavenly father stuff Nick had talked about with Jen, Kailey and I on Friday. So, I scratched that passion fuel off my mental list as a motivator for Nick.

Next, he talked about how love for God or fear of God were both motivators. How when you love someone or something, you talk about it all the time. That made some sense. But then he talked about how fear of God's judgment could also be a motivator. Sounded like a downer to me, and didn't seem like a fit for Nick.

Next up was compassion. How if you believe Jesus is the one thing everyone needs in order to experience a full, meaningful relationship with God in the midst of a messed up world full of pain and problems, compassion will fuel your passion to share God with others. Bull's eye! This was it. I could see Nick's kind, caring heart being fueled by this motivation. After all, Nick's life hadn't been an easy ride. He'd never even known his father, since he was the result of a one-night stand. Nick knew firsthand about broken relationships, plus Jesus' love and forgiveness had been at the center of his spiritual conversations with the rest of us recently.

As far as I was concerned this compassion stuff was the first time the speaker said something that remotely resembled reality. There's plenty of hell right here in this life that people need rescuing from. These fanatical preachers don't have to freak people with some scary eternal destiny hell that nobody really knows exists. Lots of people are walking through their own personal hell right now. Which explains why so many of my friends are into cutting or drinking or whatever. Even at the core of my gut, I sometimes catch an occasional glimpse of an empty abyss, a hell if you will, that's sorta unsettling. I distract myself with girls or partying or whatever, so I can just be happy and not have to think about the kind of stuff that can gnaw at you if you let it. The other day Nick had sounded like he understood all that.

FIRESTARTER

Then finally, the speaker talked about a literal hell as passion fuel. I could tell hell was the driving fuel for the speaker himself since he spent a disproportionate amount of time on this angle. He talked about telling your friends about Christ before they end up there. He read all sorts of things out of the Bible about hell and how it was an eternity in flames and suffering for all those who don't accept Christ. He described how it would be like a flame that would somehow burn our bodies forever and that we would be as consumed by the hopelessness as we were by the fire.

Not buying it.

To be honest, the guy, as sincere as he seemed, really ticked me off. Was he really trying to scare everybody into telling their friends about Jesus? In my mind, when he launched into the literal hell thing, he represented everything wrong with Christianity. I mean, who cares about the next life (if there is one at all)? It's this life that must be lived. I mean, if the "here and now" is screwed up, then who gives a rip about the "there and then?"

After describing how bad hell was, he told us to think of one particular friend who needed to know about Jesus and imagine they had died in a car accident. Jesus stuff aside, the thought of one of my friends dying in an accident was unsettling. Nick? Jen? Kailey? What a morbid thought... The speaker said to imagine you had never told your friend about Jesus and his gift of eternal life. What would they say to you from across the chasm of hell, knowing that you never told them about Jesus?

This guy was the conductor on the Guilt Trip Express and I wanted off. I wasn't the only one. When he was done, the room was silent. As I scanned the crowd, I saw a couple teenagers who were really into it, but most of the others were sending out "this is way too serious for a Sunday morning" vibes. And then I heard sniffles.

It was Kailey. She was hooked. Even Nick looked surprised as he glanced over at her.

Those sniffles turned to tears as the preacher began to snap his fingers and say, "Every second at least one person on the planet dies." SNAP "And most of them end up in hell." SNAP "And one day it will be your family member," SNAP, "your classmate," SNAP, "your teammate," SNAP, "your friend." SNAP. Kailey's eyes were locked on the speaker.

Right then a perfectly timed "you're full of crap" yawn erupted from someone in the back of the room and a smattering of giggles ensued. But this preacher would not be dissuaded…and neither would Kailey. She was mesmerized by this guy's hellfire and brimstone road show.

He then told the story about how his youth leader challenged him go to a busy shopping mall on a Saturday afternoon, sit on a bench and watch people for thirty minutes. His youth leader had him imagine a sign on everyone's forehead that read, "Bound for Hell." His voice started to crack as he shared how that exercise had impacted him. He poured out his feelings for those who didn't know Jesus, not just because of, in his words, "the hell they're headed to, but also the hell they're going through."

But then the preacher moved on from judgment and talked about the hope and forgiveness available through Jesus Christ. I found myself beginning to understand how someone like Jen or Kailey could get quickly sucked in. Even I felt a bit of a tug. I must have shook my head suddenly back and forth, like a football player trying to shake off a concussion, because Nick whispered to me, "Are you okay?"

"Just fine," I said, coming back to my senses.

But Kailey wasn't fine. I could tell she was totally all about it.

As I looked around the room, it was clear she was in the minority. Most teens were fidgeting, looking at their cell phones, rolling their eyes or just looking bored. They hadn't bought his spiel. And from the expression on the youth leader's face, it seemed to me that Eric hadn't bought it either. Maybe the hellfire scare tactics had more than just the teens looking for an exit.

When the guy was finally finished, Eric grabbed the microphone and fumbled a bit as he tried to find a tactful way to wrap it all up and distance himself from the dude.

Eric started in, "Thank you so much for sharing with us today."

FIRESTARTER

The guy next to me cracked to his friend under his breath, "What he really means is, thank you so much for scaring us today."

Eric rambled on, "I'm sure all of us know that the reality of hell is only one of many motivations for sharing Christ with your friends."

The humorous commentary next to me continued with, "Why in hell didn't you focus on one of the other ones?" This comment was now loud enough to draw snickers from several nearby teens.

Eric plowed on despite the distraction, "Whatever you think about hellfire and brimstone, just know that there are lots of sound, logical reasons for believing that Jesus loves you and your friends."

"He means, this is soooooooo embarrassing, it's time to pull out the old standby 'Jesus loves me' line," the joker cracked. More laughter erupted nearby.

By the time Eric was done, I actually kind of felt bad for the guest guy. Sure, he was a freak, but it didn't seem quite right that the Christian kids were making fun of him. As I thought about it, I wondered… if I really believed in hell and I thought that Jesus was the way out of it, would I do everything in my power to keep people out of it?

I could tell that most of these kids hadn't had many deep thoughts about all this. They didn't take the God stuff too seriously and probably never even tried to share their faith. But why even bother going to church if you don't believe this stuff? Why not sin like men and women instead of like little hypocritical wusses? At least Nick—and now maybe Jen and Kailey—seemed to take it seriously.

Eric had us bow our heads in a closing prayer, but Kailey was up and out. When we dismissed, she was talking to the hell guy in the back. She was still talking to him when we walked out of the room.

She was the only one.

March 23

I'm really glad I went to Nick's church today. The guy speaking talked about hell, the brevity of life and the urgency those two together ought to create in Christians. Somebody dies every second and there's nothing I can do to stop that. Those who don't know Jesus end up in hell. There is something I can do about that. I can at least help give them a choice. Who do I hate enough to NOT tell them how to escape hell? I need to tell everyone about the forgiveness & freedom that I've found in Jesus.

The speaker told us to imagine a "Bound for Hell" sign on the foreheads of everyone we see. After church, I went to talk with the speaker. I glanced at Jared as I walked by and saw it on his forehead in grisly red writing. It freaked me out, but it's more motivation than anything else. On the way home I saw the sign everywhere — the guy crossing the street, kids riding bikes. It nearly broke me. How could their neighbors go to church and know about Jesus and not tell them? Sharing Jesus can't be a "when you get

around to it" thing – people may not stick
around until I "get around to it."

I can't get it out of my head.

Jared is headed for hell. And if there is
anything, anything at all, I can do to change
that, I will. If I did otherwise, how could I even
call myself his friend? And not just Jared, I'm
going to talk to Emma, Heather, Elizabeth,
Garret & Michael. I'm going to do what it takes
to tell every person I can about Jesus before
it's too late. I have eight weeks before I
graduate. oh God, I still have time, right?

It tears me up that I have friends who don't
know God and are bound for hell. The speaker
guy told me I should start sharing the gospel
with everyone. God, I have no clue what to say
to them, but there's no way I'm staying silent.
These people need Jesus. Now. wow, I think this
is what God feels for those who don't believe
in him. He loves them so much he offers them
his son and the chance to be his children.

33

It must break him every time they turn him down. This ache I feel for these people is only a fraction of what GOD feels for those who don't believe in him. GOD, help me know what to say. I feel like there isn't much time and something's going to happen. Give me courage & help them to accept the truth I'm going to try to tell them about.

I'm starting first thing tomorrow morning at school...come hell or high water.

4

As I headed out to my car after school, I was surprised to find Kailey crying off to one side of the front steps. Nick was there with his arm around her, trying to comfort her. Students shuffled past, staring curiously.

Car accident? Suicide? My mind started rifling through the possible calamities. Pushing kids aside, I made my way over to Nick and Kailey.

Crouching down and putting my hand on Kailey's back, I asked, "What's happened?" She responded with sobs.

FIRESTARTER

I shot Nick a questioning look.

He whispered, "She got shut down by Emma."

"Shut down how?"

With tears streaming down her face, Kailey looked up and said haltingly between sobs, "I told Emma about the gospel and she told me to quit cramming religion down her throat. She totally blew up and said I was being a jerk." Kailey buried her face in her hands and began to cry again.

Sure she was a drama queen, the reigning drama queen of our school actually, but these tears were genuine. Relieved that it wasn't something more serious, I said, "Jen and I are meeting at Starbucks now, want to join us? Sounds like you need to talk about this over a nice, cold caramel Frappuccino."

Those two words were already working their magical mojo as she looked up and managed a slight smile. Wiping her tears with the back of her hand she said, "You probably think I'm stupid."

"Yes, I do…very, very stupid," I responded with a half smile.

She returned my serve with a punch to my shoulder and an expletive.

"Now that's not very Christian," I said with a laugh.

"Yeah, well I don't feel very Christian right now. I feel horrible."

But the mascara micro flood was subsiding enough for her to think of someone other than herself. "Am I crowding in on you and Jen by tagging along? I've noticed you two seem to be hanging out more. Do I see a budding romance developing?"

"We're hanging out more," I acknowledged casually, "but we're still dancing around it a bit."

"Better put it in high gear, lover boy, it's second semester senior year! No time to waste!" Kailey teased.

FIRESTARTER

"But summer's coming, plenty of time if the chemistry's right," I jabbed back. "Anyway, I know Jen would want you to join us at Starbucks." Turning to Nick I added, "Are you in?"

"Sure."

Minutes later, with drinks and goodies in hand, we Four Musketeers settled into a corner table. After filling Jen in briefly, I opened the investigation by quizzing Kailey, "So you ticked off Emma with all your religious talk. What did you do? Tell her about hell?"

"Yes," she said. "I told her that I didn't want to see her go to hell."

"Crap!" I sputtered, choking on my muffin. "Are you serious?"

"Yeah, I'm very serious. What that guy at church said yesterday made total sense to me. When I talked to him afterward, he told me that I should start sharing the gospel with everybody and so I decided to talk with Emma. I tried to grab her after lunch, but she had class. So, after school I brought it up again and kinda jumped to the point. That's when she blew up."

"Kinda jumped to what point?" Nick asked.

"Hell."

Nick visibly cringed. "Kailey, hell isn't the point of the gospel—Jesus is."

"Yeah, Kailey," Jen chimed in. "It was when Nick told me about Jesus' unconditional love and forgiveness and his desire to have a relationship with us, that's what grabbed my attention and touched my heart."

"Yeah, but Jesus died to save us from hell, right?" she asked.

I jumped in. "But even that guy yesterday said that Jesus died to save us from the hell we're going to *and* the hell we were going through."

They all looked at me surprised; so, I qualified, "Not that I believe that, but I was listening."

FIRESTARTER

"I'm not standing idly by while my friends are destined for hell," Kailey launched back in, her eyes blazing and her voice steeled with determination. "Today at school by my locker, I watched kids walk by and I thought about the sign on everyone's forehead that guy was talking about, 'Bound for Hell.' My heart's broken for those who don't know Jesus and I'm determined to do whatever it takes to tell as many as I can before it's too late. I've found my passion fuel."

"What's the rush?" I asked. "Nick here took four years before he finally told all of us about Jesus."

"Why *did* you take so long?" Kailey asked, turning her full focus on Nick.

Before Nick could respond, I rushed to his defense. "Well, to be fair, Nick tried to bring it up several times, but I shut him down every time."

"So, what changed last week, why were you finally ready to listen?" Kailey asked, shifting her gaze back to me.

"Hmm. That's a good question," I responded, pausing a moment to think about it. "I don't really know. I guess maybe part of it was because Jen was there and she was interested in what he had to say." I glanced over at Jen and she flashed one of her gorgeous smiles back at me. "But I do know this. I've always respected Nick. He tries to live what he believes and I guess last week seemed the right time to talk about it.

"And, although Nick was getting a little help from his youth pastor," I continued with a smile, "Jen and I listened to what he had to say because of how he lives his life and how he approached the topic. If I remember, his words were 'I'm just wanting to paint you a picture that you can choose to accept or reject.' He didn't try to cram Jesus down our throats."

"Like it sounds like you did to Emma," Nick said frankly.

Kailey's eyes started to mist over again, "I know. I know. But we only have two months before we graduate. I want to tell as many people as I can about Jesus before it's too late."

FIRESTARTER

"Ah ha! I still see that sprinter in you, girl! Everything's a competition right?" I asked.

"Yes, er, I mean no. It's not that. I just really want to share this incredible truth about Jesus with everyone, including you, Jared. Why aren't you a Christian?" she asked, switching from defense to offense.

"Hey, whoa, back off a little. I told Nick here that I'd read the book of John, but don't think for a second that I'm going to just drop to my knees and accept Jesus just because my three best friends thinks he's cool. And, to be honest, if this is the way you came at Emma, I can see why she got ticked off. And don't even start on your hell lecture, that kind of talk makes me furious. Back down, sister. Back down."

I'd seen Kailey's bulldog tenacity before, but it was rarely directed at me. This was not cool and she needed to know it. But before I could push back any further, Nick jumped in and said, "I actually agree with Jared on this one, Kailey. You can't just go around preaching at people. That doesn't work."

"Well, keeping your mouth shut doesn't work either!" Kailey said emphatically.

Jen, the conflict avoider, stayed silent.

Pulling out the Bible from his backpack, Nick flipped the pages for a few seconds before he came to the part he was looking for and read aloud, "And the Lord's servant must not quarrel; instead, he must be kind to everyone, able to teach, not resentful. Those who oppose him he must gently instruct, in the hope that God will grant them repentance leading them to a knowledge of the truth, and that they will come to their senses and escape from the trap of the devil, who has taken them captive to do his will."

We sat in silence, marinating on the words a bit. Finally, I volunteered, "I don't know jack about the Bible, but it seems to me that what Nick just read strikes the balance you're looking for here. I mean, on the one side you have the 'don't argue and be kind to everyone' stuff, and then you have the help them 'escape from the devil's pitchfork' stuff."

Nick was nodding in agreement. "Yeah, if you, I mean, if we, could find a balance between those extremes then it seems like we would have something—"

"—relational and relentless," Kailey interrupted.

"Say what?" Nick asked, looking from Kailey to me to Jen and back to Kailey again.

"I mean, that's what the stuff you just read is talking about," she explained. "If you think about it, that's kinda the difference between you and me when it comes to sharing Jesus—actually when it comes to just about everything, Nick. You're the relational guy and I'm the relentless girl."

I interrupted, "I agree. But are you saying that since you're relentless, you're going to go around relentlessly hounding everyone about Jesus all the time and that's that?"

"Not at all," Kailey replied a little defensively. "That's why I love the words Nick just read. I think they kinda balance everything out. See, I need a little more of the relational and Nick needs a little more of the relentless when it comes to sharing about Jesus."

CHAPTER 4

"Now wait a minute," I said, "Nick was plenty relentless with me."

Kailey shot back, "But he wasn't at all relentless with me or Jen. He never shared the gospel with us once. As a matter of fact, when that guy was preaching yesterday, I thought about you, Nick. If I ended up in hell, I'd be screaming, 'Why didn't you tell me about Jesus if you knew him all these years?'"

Nick's head went down. I could tell she'd struck a nerve. When he looked up, guilt had flooded his face. He said simply, "I guess I thought I had plenty of time to tell you."

"Plenty of time, Nick? We're about to graduate! And sure, we say we'll all stay in touch, but you know how that goes. By fall we'll all be off doing our own thing. We'll probably never be as close as we are right now."

"You're right," Nick acknowledged sincerely. "I should have done more sooner to tell both of you about the gospel. I'm sorry."

FIRESTARTER

Kailey put her hand on his shoulder and looking straight into his eyes said, "Well, let's not make that mistake again. We have two months before graduation and we should do our best to tell as many people as we can about Jesus before we do. And you too, Jen," she added pointedly.

"I don't know, Kailey," Nick hedged, "unless you're really close to someone, it's hard to effectively share the gospel with them. I'm just not sold on the mass marketing approach you seem to have bought into."

"Me either," Jen agreed quietly.

Kailey just sat there totally quiet, not sure what to say after they'd shot down her plan and burst her bubble. From the expression on her face, it looked like we could be replaying the crying scene she'd treated us to earlier in front of the school.

"But maybe," Nick volunteered to break the awkward silence and forestall the coming flood, "you can teach me something about being more relentless and I can teach you how to be relational. Between us we'll make a good team."

"Yeah, kind of a Clark Kent meets Lois Lane," I interjected as a release valve.

"More like Superman and Lois Lane," Nick said with a smile. "And Kailey, right up front you need to know that there are more motivations for sharing Jesus besides keeping people out of hell. Like that preacher guy said, some people share Jesus out of compassion. Like when someone's really hurting and maybe is into drinking or cutting to escape all the pain. Introducing them to Jesus can sometimes touch them at their deepest spiritual need. After all, Jesus' love for us is the greatest love story in the history of the world. And some people are motivated to share the gospel out of simple obedience to Jesus. So, you and I and Jen may have different motivations for sharing the gospel, and that's okay, as long as we're sharing the message in a loving way."

"To as many people as we can," she added. "So, how do you actually do it? Share the gospel, I mean. Can you show me how to?" Kailey asked.

"I'm not sure I know what to tell you," Nick said, looking a little embarrassed. Glancing over at me, a smile spread across his face. "Let me—"

FIRESTARTER

"—text my youth leader and ask him," I finished his sentence for him, shaking my head and laughing.

Nick took out his phone and texted Eric before Kailey resumed plotting a strategy for accomplishing her goal. Between the lines, I suspected Nick and Jen were talking about telling one or two others. But Kailey was talking about double digits, at least. I could predict there would be plenty more high drama ahead. But I was inclined to think it would be entertaining to watch the dynamic duo of Mr. Relational and Miss Relentless collide in coming days. I thought I knew Jen well enough to safely assume that she'd remain in conflict avoidance mode.

"Every Tuesday right after school," Nick said, breaking back into my thoughts, "there's a student ministry meeting on campus called CIA, that stands for Christians in Action, where interested Christians get together and talk about how to reach our campus with the gospel."

"I'm in," Kailey said nodding. "I can't wait to meet other Christians who are excited to tell others about Jesus."

"I want to go, too. How about you, Jen?" I said as they all looked at me in surprise. Quite honestly, I surprised myself. Am I crazy? Maybe all these seriously intense spiritual conversations are driving me schizo.

"Listen, uh," I fumbled around, trying to come up with some sort of plausible explanation. "Uh, I'm just interested in what's going to happen. Besides it will be fun to see everybody freak out when I show up."

But down deep inside I knew my ulterior motive. I wanted to watch the wildfire Kailey ignites burn its path of destruction. You see, I'm a provocateur at heart and I know that Kailey is, too. I love to freak people out and get them talking. I think Kailey will freak some people out too, especially the plastic Christians that wear the cheesy Christian t-shirts, gather around flagpoles and argue against evolution in science class. It'll all be quite entertaining.

FIRESTARTER

Nick's phone vibrated with an incoming text. "From Eric," he announced before he read it. "Can you meet at the church in twenty minutes? Do you have time now, Kailey? I do."

"Let's do it," she said eagerly.

Jen and I bowed out, opting to stay at Starbucks together for a while longer.

Kailey and Nick grabbed their drinks and headed to their cars. Clearly, this was all going to provide me with some front row entertainment during the last two months of school. As they pulled out of the parking lot, I had the thought that they might want to keep checking their side view mirrors. Conflict may be closer than it appears.

It feels good to be so bad.

March 24

I tried talking to Emma today. I'm glad that I had the courage to walk up to her, but things didn't turn out so hot. She said I was a jerk for telling her about hell. I still think I'd be more of a jerk not to tell her. The whole situation really got to me, because she could end up in hell unless something big changes. When she walked away, I started crying a little, I felt so powerless. And then Nick came over to see what was wrong and when I started talking about Emma and hell I couldn't help but start bawling.

We four Musketeers went to Starbucks afterward. I think they wanted to cheer me up. I don't know what I'd do without friends like them. They helped talk some sense into me about my approach too. We came up with this idea of sharing Jesus in a "relational and relentless" way. I like it. Just straight out telling people about hell, like I did with Emma, doesn't really seem to work, but I'm not going to sit back & wait for the perfect

51

opportunity. I need to be sharing the truth of Jesus' sacrifice and love all the time, not just every once in awhile. At this point in our conversation, the question of <u>how</u> to share our faith became the next big roadblock to our plan.

So Nick & I drove over to his church to talk to his youth leader Eric pulled out this red & white "field guide" book and we got this thing called an acrostic from it where the first letter of each word spells out GOSPEL:

God created us to be with him.

Our sins separate us from GOD.

Sins cannot be removed by good deeds.

Paying the price for sins, Jesus died and rose again.

Everyone who trusts in him alone has eternal life.

Life with Jesus starts now and lasts forever!

At first, it sorta seemed like a script my drama
director would give me. I sat there in Eric's office
imagining myself spouting some little memorized
presentation like a robot. Hmmm, maybe I could
just sing it like Sandra D? Then again, I can't
imagine Emma would appreciate that.

Then Eric told me the goal of this wasn't to give
me a script, but a guide. He said I should
memorize it and then personalize it, weaving in
my own experiences of God's power and goodness.
The end goal is to have a conversation with
someone about God. Eric also recommended a
series of podcasts about sharing your faith, so
I've been watching those tonight. I'm realizing
there is so much I don't know about Christianity.
But the guy on the podcast said if I don't have
an answer when I'm talking to someone, I should
say, "I don't know, but I'll find out." Then I'll
study the Bible, text Eric or ask Nick for the
answer.

So I've spent my evening practicing the gospel
using the little acrostic as a framework until it
was genuine - my story & God's story put
together. I'm determined to tell as many people

as I can about Christ before school gets out. ALL DAY I saw the sign "BOUND FOR HELL" on people's foreheads. I Just can't get it out of my head. oh, and I'm not giving up on Emma. I blew it today, but there's always tomorrow! well, that's the hope anyway...

Nick, JareD, Jen & I are going to the CIA meeting — a meeting of christian students — after school tomorrow. yeah, <u>JareD</u> is coming too. That's a good sign, right? I'm really worried about him. Anyway, I'm excited to hear about what other christians at our school are Doing to tell their friends about Jesus.

5

The room was already abuzz when I walked in and Kailey was in the center of it all. The wildfire I had predicted was quickly burning out of control. I could kick myself that I'd missed the first twenty minutes of the afterschool Bible-thumper meeting.

About twenty-five people were in the room and Mrs. Swenson, the girls' volleyball coach, was trying to get control back. An angry vibe permeated the room and it was clear that the sparks had been lit by Kailey. There was an intensity in her eyes as she struggled to get everyone's attention.

FIRESTARTER

"Okay, everybody calm down! Calm down! I think Kailey wants to apologize," Mrs. Swenson announced.

"I'm sorry, Mrs. Swenson, but I don't apologize for what I said. This meeting does seem stupid to me. But I would like to explain myself."

"Okay," Mrs. Swenson said.

"Well, I became a Christian on Saturday, went to church for the first time on Sunday and am here today, so I'm kind of new to this whole Christianity thing. But I seriously don't understand what good this meeting is. Maybe that's why you call this meeting CIA. You've certainly been successful at keeping it undercover, hiding here in a back room of the school."

Bryan, the quarterback of the football team (okay, so not all Christians are dorks) interrupted defensively, "I'll tell you why we're here, Kailey. We're here to fellowship, worship God, pray and learn from the Bible."

"Yeah," Kailey shot back, "that's what I don't understand. Isn't that what church is for? I thought this meeting would be more about saving our friends from hell."

From the back of the room, I could see Nick, face bright red, sitting next to Kailey trying not to make eye contact with anyone.

"Saving them from hell?" Bryan asked with a look of genuine confusion on his face.

"Do you mean evangelism—sharing your faith?" Mrs. Swenson asked.

"Yeah, evangelism," Kailey affirmed. "Like I said, I don't know all the terms yet."

Bryan commandeered the conversation like he was used to calling the plays, "Well, Kailey, that's part of what we do, but that's not all we do. There are other priorities."

"Which one of those priorities can't be accomplished at your church?" Kailey fired back. Silence. You could've heard a pin drop. "I'm not trying to make anybody mad, but I'm beginning to wonder if you guys really care about people who don't know Jesus. I've been going to this school for four years and not one of you ever told me about Jesus. I don't understand that. If I had cancer and you had the cure to cancer, you'd share it with me, right?" Kailey borrowed Nick's metaphor. I'm not sure how he felt about that. He was still sitting next to her, motionless.

"RIGHT????" she said again louder.

"Yeah," Bryan agreed quietly. It felt like Kailey might actually be starting to tap into some emotional/spiritual vibe in the room. Nick was nodding in agreement now, instead of hiding in embarrassment. What a weird dynamic.

She continued, "Well, the people at our school have something worse than cancer and they're headed somewhere worse than death and we have the cure!" Looking around the room she said, "Seems to me you've been hiding that cure in this room every Tuesday at 3 p.m."

Bryan said defensively, "Several times a year we do outreaches that we invite our friends to."

"That's true," Nick agreed, glancing uncertainly at Kailey.

"But," I blurted loudly without even thinking, "if that's your plan, it's not working." Everyone now noticed that I was in the room. With all eyes turned on me, I was enjoying the confusion on their faces as they tried to figure out what exactly I was doing there.

"What do you know about it, anyway?" Bryan jumped back in, his competitive juices rising. "Last year we had thirty-five people trust in Christ through our outreaches."

Kailey, always quick with a comeback, said, "Well, where are they, then?" Scanning the room she asked, "How many of you became a Christian through one of the outreaches this group's done?"

Four people raised their hands.

FIRESTARTER

Refocusing her eyes on Bryan she said, "I think that's awesome, Bryan. But it's not enough. There are 2,100 kids at this school and we can't tell them about Jesus hiding in this back room."

"What do you suggest?" Mrs. Swenson asked. She'd long since given up wrestling control of the conversation back from Kailey.

"I suggest we tell them all."

A handful of people laughed outright at this comment and most of the rest snickered cynically.

Wrong move. Kailey has a temper. This was going to be fun.

"Do you think that's funny?" she charged. I could tell she was trying hard to keep her cool.

"Kind of," one teen shot back. "Do you really think you're going to singlehandedly talk to everyone in this school in the next two months?"

"No," Kailey said, taking a deep breath to calm down, "I'll need some help."

CHAPTER 5

"What kind of help?" Bryan asked.

"Well, I figure if we had enough Christians at this school who would just talk to their friends about Jesus, we could reach most everyone," Kailey responded, "especially if we could show the new ones who trust in Jesus how to share their faith with their friends."

"Kind of like an evangelism epidemic," Bryan responded, starting to get the picture. "So, what you're talking about is us sharing the gospel ourselves?"

"Yes!" Kailey said, clearly pumped. "Isn't that what evangelism is? Why do we have to bring them somewhere to hear about Jesus, anyway? Everyone I know is busy. Between sports schedules, drama practice, friends and homework, who has time for some extracurricular spiritual meeting, whether it's this or some church meeting?"

"So, you're suggesting we cancel all of these meetings and never invite friends to outreach meetings?" Mrs. Swenson asked tersely.

FIRESTARTER

"No, I guess what I'm saying is that I think we should be driving those spiritual conversations, instead of depending on adults like you to do it all for us," Kailey responded.

Nick smiled politely at Mrs. Swenson and tried to clarify, "I think all Kailey's saying is that we should be having these conversations with our friends at lunch, in the hallway, after school, online—wherever."

"Yeah," Kailey agreed, "and if you want to invite them to an outreach meeting as part of helping them understand the gospel, that's fine, but we shouldn't depend on outreach meetings to do the work for us."

"I get it, sorta like we're the walking, talking outreach meeting everywhere we go?" Bryan asked.

"Yes! That's what I'm trying to say! We're the outreach meeting!" Kailey said. "Who's in?"

Only Kailey, Nick, Bryan and a nerdy underclassman wearing a "Smile Jesus Loves You" t-shirt raised their hands—an unlikely "crew" of four to turn the school upside down for Jesus. I noticed Jen didn't raise her hand. Glad to see she had a mind of her own.

"Well, I'd say that's certainly a success." The snide remark had come from the guy beside me, but he echoed my thoughts precisely.

"It's enough to start with," Kailey responded without a trace of anger. She was surprisingly upbeat. "Let's meet tomorrow over lunch to make our plan."

"So, does this mean that you won't be joining us next week, Kailey?" Mrs. Swenson asked.

"I'll be back if I have time," Kailey responded. "But my priority is to share Jesus with my friends during the week, not bring them to a meeting, and if I do bring them, you can be sure I'll have already started the conversation about Jesus."

March 25

we went to CIA after school today. It wasn't what I expected it to be. It's seemed very ~~tame~~ cliquish. Definitely not very serious about sharing Jesus. But Nick & I talked enough to get a couple other students to commit to lunch together tomorrow. I'm excited! I think this could be the start of something really cool.

Mrs. Swenson pulled me aside afterwards. I thought I was in for it since I'd argued with her during the meeting. But she said she admired my determination and wanted to make sure I "stayed Biblical and didn't get carried away." For all my enthusiasm today, I know I'm still a beginner at all of this. I'm up for any advice I can get. She told me to read Colossians 4:4-6 and pray about it. It speaks right to all this!

"Pray that I may proclaim it clearly, as I should. Be wise in the way you act toward outsiders; make the most of every opportunity. Let your conversation be always full of grace, seasoned with salt, so that you may know how to answer everyone."

I see what she's talking about. Sharing Jesus isn't about uttering some script and scaring/scarring people. I made that mistake with Emma. I need to be deliberate & careful in my words, and the best way to do that is through prayer. God got me to this place of peace that I'd never been able to find on my own before. He wants other people here too, which means He knows best how to get them there. I need to tap into his plans for their lives and help out however I can. And the only way I can hope to do that is through prayer. That shouldn't be too hard — ever since Saturday, I've found myself praying at random moments throughout the day. I can't keep silent toward a God I love, and who loves me soooo much. But those Colossians verses help remind me that I need to pray for my friends as well as have conversations with them.

ummm...so, rather than being mad at me, I wonder if deep down inside Mrs. Swenson was intrigued by my attitude. I sensed that maybe my comments sparked something inside her that had been hibernating for awhile. Maybe she really knows that something is broken in the way this group's been going. Maybe everybody knows and they're just afraid to admit it.

I'm excited about lunch. Again, Jared is coming. I can't help but think that he feels some sort of pull toward God. I want him & my other friends to know God's love & forgiveness so much it hurts sometimes. I hope I can help people understand how to escape hell and find the indescribable love of Jesus. I don't want to leave this school untouched by God's love.

i'm going to PRAY
PRAY
PRAY!

6

The school cafeteria was bustling. It was chilly outside for SoCal; so, the kids who weren't flocking to Taco Bell were slamming sloppy joes, the fifth food group, down their throats.

"Mind if I join you?" I asked as I approached a table where the four Bible club crazies were gathered—plus Jen. I was glad to see her there to keep me company.

"Not at all, Jared," Kailey said with a smile, "but we're making our plans."

FIRESTARTER

"I'll try to be good," I responded. "What the heck, maybe I can give you advice on how to approach hard-core pagans like me."

Bryan laughed awkwardly. I sensed he was uncomfortable with my presence and surprised by my comment.

"Well, here's what we have so far. Right now, we're calling it our circle of friends," Kailey explained pointing to her notebook. She'd drawn a circular set of three arrows and written several names inside the circle.

"Ha, I made the list!" I observed.

"It's just a way to identify all your friends, from best friends to teammates and drama compatriots, so you can reach them all."

"And how exactly are you going to do that?" I asked.

"We're going to pray for them, bring God up and convince them that Jesus is the way," Kailey responded, pointing back to the three arrows on her little illustration.

Pointing to the word "Pray," Nick said, "The first step is to pray every day for all of our friends who don't know Jesus."

"I think you might need a bigger circle," I said, amused by their little strategy session. "I just heard somewhere recently that the average teenager has 53 friends—that's including online friends. That seems like a lot of people to pray for every day," I added skeptically. "Not that I actually know anything about praying."

David, the weird, nerdy kid, suggested quietly, "Maybe you could start with three friends you'd pray for daily and try to talk to about the gospel."

"What do you mean 'you'? I thought you were in this with us?" Bryan challenged.

"Well, the thing is, I don't really have any non-Christian friends. I just transferred this semester from a Christian school 'cause my parents couldn't afford tuition anymore. The few friends I've made here at Brentwood are all Christians."

"Kid, just go through your cell phone contact list or your MySpace and Facebook friends, there must be people you know who aren't Christians," I said.

"And if there aren't, go make some friends," Kailey added. "Think about teenagers in your neighborhood, make some more friends online."

"I don't use MySpace or Facebook," David said, embarrassed.

"Start thinking of them as outreach tools to make friends and then share Jesus," Bryan interjected, adding emphasis to his words by pounding David on the back with a gusto only a football player could get away with. Guess it was better than a slap on the butt.

"Yeah, and don't forget about the teens you have around you every day," Kailey said looking up at the crowded cafeteria and pointing in a circle around the cafeteria. "Make some friends here."

"I'm not really good at that," David responded, eyes turned downward.

I was thinking what a pathetic little nerd he was when kind-hearted Jen came to his rescue. "My mom gave me some great advice about making friends at school. She told me that people love to talk about themselves, and so to make lots of friends, you should ask them questions about their interests, passions, hobbies and stuff like that. And be genuinely interested in them and their answers."

Checking the time Kailey said, "We only have a few more minutes before class, let's get this nailed down. So, we write down the names of all of our friends and start praying for the three we want to share the gospel with first, right?"

"Yeah," Nick affirmed. "Maybe we can draw three lines above 'Pray' and write in the names of those we're praying for."

Kailey drew the lines and put the names of the three friends she was going to start with. I felt an uncomfortable twinge at the sight of my name at the very top of her list.

FIRESTARTER

Nick continued, "And as soon as you bring God up in conversation with them, you can move them over to the 'Bring Up' part of the circle." Even I could see the logic behind this systematic approach.

"So when you transfer a name from 'Pray' to 'Bring Up' you should plug in a new name and start praying for someone else, right?" asked Kailey.

"You better use a pencil or it's going to get messy," David added.

"So, it would look like this," Kailey said, making the changes to her illustration and pushing it forward so everyone could see.

"So, you keep pulling up names from your circle of friends to pray for every day, and when you actually start bringing God up in one way or another, you move them here," Nick said, pointing. "And I guess you move them again when you start to convince them about Jesus. What's cool is that this could be a kind of spiritual tracking device to help you know where you're at when it comes to actually reaching all your friends for Jesus."

CHAPTER 6

David interrupted, "What does it take to make an app for an iPhone? There must be some way to adapt this electronically and make it easier. "

"Go for it," Kailey said. "That would be immensely cool—not that I have an iPhone…"

"Maybe I will," David said, scratching his head.

"I have a question," I interrupted.

"What is it atheist, I mean, Jared?" Kailey said playfully.

"What are you trying to convince them of?"

"Well, we're trying to convince them that Jesus is the way!" Kailey shot back.

"Is that all?" I asked, being totally serious. "Yesterday you were talking about telling others about Jesus and then getting them to tell their friends. Remember the 'evangelism epidemic?'"

FIRESTARTER

"He's right," Nick said. "That's going to be what makes this thing go. After all, we only have two months until school's out."

"So, what are we trying to convince people of?" Kailey asked, leaning back and looking up.

Busy scribbling, David said, "I know." Then looking up, he pushed a piece of paper across the white gloss of the cafeteria table. It had three short phrases on it with the first letter of every phrase scribbled over a couple times to bold them:

Accept Christ.

Belong to a church.

Commit to this cause.

"I love it!" Nick said. "David, you're brilliant! That's what we're trying to convince them to do, to believe in Jesus, to belong to the body of Christ and then to join us in this cause!"

"*This* cause?" Kailey pushed back. "This is *THE* Cause."

"What do you mean?" I asked.

"Well, I've always been a 'cause' kind of girl. From social justice stuff to environmentalism—" Kailey said before I interrupted her.

"—yeah, you're the one who proposed the 'Hug the Planet' theme for the prom. I'm so glad that one bit the dust, enviro-girl."

Kailey stuck her tongue out at me before continuing, "It's true, and I'm still passionate about that stuff. But, in the eternal scheme of things, this is way more important."

Nick and David nodded in agreement.

"So, saving the planet from global warming may be important, but saving people from eternal 'warming' in hell is even more important?" I joked.

But my little green joke turned red from embarrassment in this crowd. Kailey simply said, "Yes," with a look of determination in her eyes. Other than Jen and I, this crew was serious and focused,

FIRESTARTER

like a special-ops team taking on a daring new assignment.

Kailey took the piece of paper, crossed out "this" and wrote "THE" in big, bold caps above it. "Commit to THE Cause." Then she pushed the paper back out to the middle of the table and said, "And we can call our circle of friends we're trying to share Jesus with 'THE Cause Circle.'"

We all looked at the circular drawing. "Everyone in?" Kailey asked glancing around the table.

"Nope," I stated categorically, while Jen quietly shook her head 'no.' But everyone else was in.

"Hey guys, tonight is youth group. Let's run it by Eric and see what he thinks," Nick said.

Holy crap, how often do these Christians meet? Sunday morning, Tuesday after school, Wednesday night, and the week is still young.

"Sorry to disappoint, but I can't come tonight," I said.

"I can," Kailey responded. "I really want to see what Eric thinks. He seems like he has a lot of experience with this sort of stuff." Like a coach calling the plays, Kailey continued, "Okay, everybody go home and fill out your Cause Circle tonight and pick the first three people you're going to talk to about Jesus and start praying for them."

Everyone nodded...except me and Jen.

"Why don't we pray real quick? I've got to get to class," Bryan said.

All the Christians bowed in prayer while Bryan prayed out loud. I sat there with my arms folded and my eyes wide open, scanning this unlikely crew who were determined to "take their school for Christ" in two months: a fresh-from-Christian-school dweeb, a lifelong Christian friend, a football quarterback and a freshly converted and overtly determined drama queen.

Perfect. Simply perfect.

March 26

Gah! I don't understand Eric. Yesterday he seemed so stoked to teach us his acrostic for sharing Jesus and today he told us we were being too aggressive and that I was going to drive people away from Jesus. Yeah, I get that my tactics with Emma were a little severe, but we don't have all the time in the world! My time here is limited, and I want to impact as many people as I can with the good news of Jesus!

Okay, a little back story. Eric was telling Nick & me about Acts 8 where Phillip ran up beside this chariot and asked the guy in it, who was reading something from the Bible, if he understood what he was reading. Eric said it was key that Phillip didn't just jump in, that he waited until he was invited up. Nick & I looked at each other, smiled and said, "Relational and Relentless." I definitely agree with Eric there, but where we don't see eye to eye is in defining what "jumping in" actually looks like. He thinks that "running by the chariot" is living lives that please God and serve others - that we should share the gospel only when our friends invite us to.

waiting around doesn't sit well with me at all. So, I told Eric that, yeah, we should live godly lives, but that we might not have time to wait! I reminded him of the speaker on Sunday about how we don't know when our friends would die. I even showcased a few of my own snaps. Eric said that there were quite a few complaints about this guy's talk and he has some of his own, since he's convinced that patient, logical reasoning is a better approach than "hell scare tactics." He said that the speaker meant well but went a little overboard.

So what if he did? Maybe he needed to. If hell is real, then we should be doing everything we can to keep people out. And if heaven's real, then we should be doing everything we can to get people in. Seems to me that if Jesus is real, then there isn't anything we shouldn't do to get people into a relationship with him.

The other thing I don't understand is how Christians treat me. It's like they think I'm weird for wanting to share Jesus and save people from hell. It's difficult to even begin to count the number of dirty looks I've gotten in the last couple days. I don't understand why sharing Jesus isn't more important to them.

79

Maybe they've just settled into an easy routine, or they've been forced to go to church all their lives. I guess they've never really gotten the sheer amazingness of the message of Jesus. If they remembered the hopelessness of what a life without God is like...I remember that feeling all too well. I'm glad it's gone now. Gosh, God is amazing.

I started reading the New Testament, like Nick suggested, and every time Jesus walks on the scene he takes my breath away. He never seems ashamed to bring up the truth, even if it makes people uncomfortable.

"When he saw the crowds, he had compassion on them, because they were harassed and helpless, like sheep without a shepherd. Then he said to his disciples, "The harvest is plentiful but the workers are few. Ask the Lord of the harvest, therefore, to send out workers into his harvest field" (from Matthew 9).

I just finished reading Matthew 9 and a couple things hit me. wow, to think that God would "have compassion" on us! Jesus' compassion is one of the things that drives me to this work. (I'm one of the workers, right?) His heart broke over those who didn't know him as their savior. Maybe when he saw the crowds he saw the sign too: Bound for Hell.

I don't think Eric sees the sign.

Don't get me wrong, I think Eric means well, but if he believes in hell & heaven & the gospel & all that, but isn't willing to put it out there and challenge the teenagers in his youth group to do the same, then maybe he's a hypocrite.

Or maybe I'm just being too hard on him. I don't know.

Anyway, even after the rocky start to our conversation tonight, Eric seemed interested (maybe even a little sentimental...) when we were showing him our little Pray-Bring Up-Convince circle and talking about our plan to talk to our friends and then mobilize them to talk to their friends. After looking at the

81

Diagram for a little while, Eric said the circle might help the whole youth group think purposefully about evangelism!!! He wants to use it for the whole youth group! We could really expand THE cause quickly if he was fully on board! Whoa, I'm getting ahead of myself.

Anyway, Eric copied the circle onto his own sheet of paper and then asked if we minded if he changed the wording a little to make it easier to remember. Sure, whatev. After a little thought, he wrote some words down and showed them to Nick & me for our approval. I think I like his better than ours. Pray. Pursue. Persuade. So, here's my newest plan of action.

THE Cause Circle

Elizabeth ~~Jared~~
Emma
Heather

PRAY

Emma

Nicole

Jared

Elizabeth

Michael

Heather

Garret

ANDY

PERSUADE

PURSUE

Michelle

JARED

83

Eric said something else that resonated with me. He told us that we won't even really make a dent without the power of God. He read us a verse from Philippians 4:13, "I can do everything through Christ who strengthens me." And, as I think about what we're trying to do, I know I'm going to need Jesus' strength.

Eric also talked to us about Acts 1:8, "But you shall receive power when the Holy Spirit comes on you; and you will be my witnesses..." I really didn't understand much about the Holy Spirit stuff; so, I quizzed Nick more afterwards. Nick said he heard once that the Holy Spirit is kinda like the spark plug in an engine. Being a car buff he went on and on about how in a real engine the sparkplug creates the spark in the engine thing-a-ma-jig to ignite the fuel and create some kind of mini-explosion in the chamber or whatever and that creates the power to turn the pistons which crank the other thing-a-ma-jigs which move the car.

Nick then related it all to the Holy Spirit. He explained that while we bring the passion fuel that motivates us to share our faith - like with me, my passion fuel is the reality of hell - we still need the Holy Spirit to be the spark that ignites our efforts and infuses them with the explosive power needed to start the engine and get the vehicle moving. I get it now that the Holy Spirit is going to have to give me the power to share the gospel in a relational and relentless way. He's going to have to open up the hearts of my friends who think Christianity is just some ancient myth.

So I'm praying for my "three" - Jared, Emma & Heather - like crazy and I'm going to pray every day that the Holy Spirit will ignite the cause and make it explode at school. I have to pray because I really have no clue how to do this whole cause thing. Nick had called it the Great ~~Condition~~ Commission once, whatever that is. However you name it, one reality is true - without God helping, this thing could never be done. But, to be honest, with God's help I feel unstoppable.

As God helps us talk to our friends, and then encourage them to talk to their friends, and on and on, then every teen can hear the gospel from a friend they know & trust. I don't care if it is a bit extreme - people at least need to be presented with the opportunity to choose God & salvation. And at least I'll be able to sleep at night knowing that I did my best to tell as many people as I could before I graduate. I'm really excited that four of us from lunch are actually going to follow through and "PRAY - PURSUE - PERSUADE" our friends!

7

For the entire next week, Kailey, Nick, Bryan and David worked hard to talk to their Cause Circle, one by one. I was on both Nick and Kailey's hit lists and they repeatedly tried to bring God up in conversations with me, but whenever it got personal, I quickly shut them down. I was watching them all intently and mischievously.

I actually found it amusing that they were struggling to execute their plan. This was turning out to be harder than they'd thought. If it hadn't been for Kailey's relentless drive and determined cheerleading, I think the rest of the group would have bagged it and retreated back to their safe, secure Tuesday CIA meeting.

But they continued to meet every day at lunch to pray and share about different spiritual conversations they were having with their teammates and classmates. It wasn't really a meeting. It was just a group of friends swapping stories, sharing challenges and asking questions. And I guess they were learning as they went, because toward the beginning of their second week of efforts, there were three or four new kids who'd become Jesus followers and joined in on THE Cause.

While I was still determined to keep my distance from God and the whole Savior Jesus thing, I did join their gatherings off and on just out of curiosity. After that first meeting Jen had always declined to come with me for these lunches, which kinda bothered me. After all, she was the one who was a Christian. You'd think she'd have some interest in what Kailey and Nick were up to.

So, one day I decided to drill down and try to understand why she was so resistant.

"I thought I'd go check in on the Jesus freaks today at lunch. Want to join me?" I asked, testing the waters.

"Not really," she stated flatly. I could almost see a protective mask drop down over her face.

"Help me understand where you're at with this Jesus stuff these days, Jen. I don't know where you're coming from on this."

"I love knowing Jesus and I love that he's forgiven me and that I'm going to heaven. And I love how God the Father is the perfect heavenly Daddy who is so different from my earthly Dad. But all this beating the bushes to drum up more Jesus followers, I'm just not into that. That's not at all what I signed up for when I decided to become a Christian. And another thing, I'm not going to reduce my friendships to a list of targets like THE Cause crew is doing. It's almost like they're a hit squad out to blast away everyone they know with their Bible bullets. I'm just not interested in that. Not my thing at all. And besides," she continued hesitantly, lowering her voice, "I'm not going to risk my popularity over THE Cause."

FIRESTARTER

"What do you mean by the popularity thing?"

"Just because Kailey's dead set on recruiting everyone to Christianity before graduation, doesn't mean I'm going to risk my image."

Stepping onto treacherous ground, I decided to speak up for Kailey. This was a risky move, since Jen was my main interest these days. Speaking from experience, I knew that defending one girl against another left you wide open to trouble, but I was concerned that a major breakup among our Four Musketeers was on the horizon. That would be a shame, since we were just a few weeks from graduation. So, I stepped up to defend Kailey and chose my words carefully. "I can't believe I'm saying this, but I don't think Kailey's goal is to recruit everyone to Christianity. She just wants to make sure she's giving everyone she knows a chance to make a choice and she's encouraging all you Christians to do the same."

"Yeah, yeah. Whatever," Jen said coolly. "All I know is if I start bringing this stuff up with my friends in dance, I'll get laughed at and rejected. I can't take that. I won't do that. It's just not worth it to me."

I could see she was upset about all this. "Well, no matter what," I assured her, "you know I'm still here for you, and I'm sure Kailey and Nick would say the same."

"I'm not so sure about them. If they find out how I feel, they may not accept me anymore."

"Well, they accept me and I'm an atheist!"

"Yeah, well, they're still trying to get you into the fold," she responded. "Whatever you do, promise me you won't say anything to Nick or Kailey about this conversation."

"Sure," I said as the bell rang and we headed to class.

Then at lunch I broke my promise and filled Nick in right away. Hey, don't judge me for lying. I'm an atheist and we supposedly don't believe in absolutes, right?

"Why do you think Jen is so freaked out about sharing her faith with her friends?" I asked.

FIRESTARTER

"Probably the same reason most Christians freak out about it," Nick replied. When he started flipping Bible pages, I knew I was about to get a verse or two. My cringe factor over Nick's Bible stuff was still pretty high, but I tried to listen patiently as he read from John chapter 12, "'Yet at the same time many even among the leaders believed in him'—it's talking about Jesus here," Nick clarified. "'But because of the Pharisees they would not confess their faith for fear they would be put out of the synagogue; for they loved praise from men more than praise from God.'

"Even back in Jesus' day," Nick explained, "there were true believers who were too afraid to share their faith because of what others would think about them. They were believers, not disciples. Only disciples are willing to pick up the cross of dying to themselves and getting mocked by others like Jesus did. Jen probably hasn't come to the point in her life as a believer where she's willing to sacrifice everything, including her popularity, to follow after Christ. If she can grow to that point, she'll be rewarded by God both now and forever."

Sounded like a load of crap to me, but Nick really believed it. And, although I don't believe in Jesus, I do respect Nick. After lunch, Nick pulled Kailey into the picture and together they approached Jen and assured her that she was absolutely still their good friend, regardless of where she stood with THE Cause.

"You can approach this whole sharing Jesus thing as fast or as slow as you want—or not at all," Nick had assured Jen, as Kailey nodded her agreement, "and you'll still be one of the Four Musketeers."

Then out of nowhere on a bright, spring morning, tragedy struck at Brentwood High. I remember clearly that the clock in senior English read 8:21 when the principal came on the intercom with a sobering announcement. "We received the sad and unexpected news this morning that one of our student body members passed away yesterday. Senior Matthew Cromby died last night. Because of the disturbing nature of this loss to our school family, we have made arrangements to have extra counselors available…" The announcement droned on, but I tuned out as I listened to the quite whispers permeating the room around me. The whispers added a disturbing detail that the principal had discreetly avoided in his announcement—Matt's death was a suicide.

I knew Matt pretty well. He was one of the last kids I would ever think of as being suicidal. He was smart, personable and had plenty of friends. His family seemed normal when I'd been over to his house to do a group project a month ago. This couldn't have happened on purpose. Maybe he'd mistakenly overdone it on pain meds or sleeping pills. Or maybe he was a cutter and sliced too deep by mistake. He couldn't have planned it out, right? I saw him smiling yesterday. I wonder if there was a note. It all seems so out of the blue. And what's really unsettling is that it makes me wonder about my occasional flashes of lonely emptiness and vague feelings of purposelessness. Could they ever morph into monsters that would overwhelm me and push me into that kind of hopelessness?

Looking around the room, I could tell I wasn't the only one thinking these kinds of thoughts. Most of the girls were crying and most of the guys looked shell-shocked. Matt was in this very English class. I and a couple others were eyeing his empty desk a couple rows away. The desk reminded all of us that we'd failed Matt. A kind word, or a phone call at the right time, who knows what might have tipped the balance in the right direction for him. As the announcement ended, the suicide news had swept the whole room. Everyone stayed where they were, processing this tragedy.

"How could this happen?" the girl behind me asked no one in particular. "How could Matt not know that he had people to turn to instead of…this?"

"How could his life have been so unbearable?" one of the guys asked morbidly.

"What'd we do wrong?" another girl said, sobbing uncontrollably.

"How could he not know that he could always turn to God when he felt like everyone else had let him down?" Nick added quietly from the seat beside me.

I could tell Mr. Davis, our English teacher, was shook up, too. But he managed to pull himself together enough to say, "We're all going to miss

FIRESTARTER

Matt and we'll probably never know what Matt's tipping point was, but it's not our fault. I also want to be very, very clear about one thing. In these kinds of situations, it's not unusual for there to be copycat suicides. When a death like this hits a school, it plants the idea in other students' heads as a way to escape whatever they might be struggling with. So I want you to utilize the counselors the principal was talking about. Even if it's not them, make sure you talk to someone. Also, have conversations with your friends in the coming days to make sure everyone's doing okay. Every single student at Brentwood needs to know that they're loved. And if you encounter something you aren't sure how to deal with either personally or with one of your friends, it's absolutely essential that you get an adult involved."

"How could Matt not know that he could always turn to God when he felt like everyone else had let him down?" Nick repeated again. "Kailey's right, everyone needs the chance to hear about Jesus. We have to get the word out. This is urgent. You never know when it's going to be too late."

When class dismissed, Nick and I headed to Jen's locker. We found her there, slumped on the floor, arms curled around some textbook, sobbing her heart out. I reached down and pulled her up and wrapped her gently in my arms. I really didn't trust myself to say anything just then, fearing I would dissolve into tears, too. It was Nick who finally helped Jen get control when he said, "Jen, I can see now that Kailey's urgency about sharing Jesus is right. Every student at Brentwood needs the chance to hear about Jesus and the love and hope he offers. We have to spread the word. And we have to do it now, because you never know when it's going to be too late."

Jen quietly nodded her agreement.

It quickly became apparent that other Christian teens were reaching the same conclusion, because five new faces showed up at the lunch meeting that day. Throughout the week, THE Cause crew kept getting bigger. On the occasions when I listened in on their lunchtime gatherings, everybody brought new stories and new ideas about engaging friends in spiritual discussions. Some passed out books to their friends that explained Christianity, asked their friends to read them and then followed up with a "What did you think?" But most of them would just bring it up. They would ask their friends questions like, "So what do you believe about God?" or "What are your spiritual beliefs?" or "Do you know for sure you're going to heaven when you die?" or whatever. And, most of the time, their friends would actually seem to want to share their opinions about all this stuff.

I was still an unbiased observer, but I knew I was watching a social phenomenon begin to unfold. Because of Matt's suicide, students were open to talking about spiritual things like what gives life hope and meaning and what happens after you die. It seemed the destructive wildfire I'd predicted Kailey would ignite had instead morphed into a spiritual blaze that was starting to light the darkness. And while Kailey was the initial spark for the fire now burning brightly, I sensed this blaze was being fueled by something bigger than the sum of its parts.

Kailey was taking this all so seriously that she had listened to an entire podcast series on evangelism, and once she'd finished it, she was even more excited, and what was scarier, more equipped. She was absorbing all this Jesus stuff like a sponge, determined she wouldn't need to text secret SOS messages to Eric in the midst of her spiritual conversations with friends. And whatever she learned, she passed on to her peers. One day I heard her going on and on about discovering your own sharing style. She was really pumped by the idea that God designed different people with different natural inclinations when it came to sharing the gospel. The four categories were talkers, "stalkers," buddies and brains. It was obvious to me that Nick was a buddy, while Kailey was a "stalker." She was never hesitant about bringing God up with me.

———————

Two weeks after Matt's death, THE Cause crew was still growing and they decided they shouldn't even try to meet as one cohesive group anymore. Instead, smaller clusters formed to encourage each other and to learn how to share their faith with their friends. Then these kids took the message to their natural cliques. Kailey came up with the idea of organizing a Facebook group where everyone from these smaller groups could share stories and ideas online. These guys were serious. They all seemed

FIRESTARTER

to be trying to feed the fire as the clock was ticking down the days before the end of school. How weird was that? Instead of being overcome by spring fever or senioritis, they were acting like each day was slipping away through their fingers.

But it wasn't all sweetness and light. THE Cause crew was leaving some carnage behind in the path of the blaze as well. There was Bryan's friend, Dan, who told Bryan he didn't want to have anything to do with him if Jesus was the only thing he was going to talk about. Dan told all of their friends that Bryan had turned into some kind of Jesus freak and they'd dropped him cold.

There was Garret, Kailey's gay friend and fellow thespian. He took Kailey's acceptance of Jesus as a rejection of him. She tried to salvage the friendship, but he viewed her "Jesus as the only way to heaven" talk as hate speech. He was sure Kailey would hate him now, and from what I read on the internet about "evangelical Christianity," I was thinking he was probably right.

Some of the teachers and administration weren't happy with Kailey and crew either. I heard through the grapevine that the drama teacher gave Kailey a stern talking to for talking about Jesus during class. I wish I'd been there to see that one. At one point admin even tried to douse the flames and ban some of the small student gatherings, but Mrs. Swenson took a stand for Kailey and crew and got the principal to back down. Mrs. Swenson seemed to have had a bit of a change of heart, because she pulled Kailey aside one day in the hall and told her she was praying for THE Cause. She even asked if there was anything she could do to help.

But on the youth group front, I got the impression Eric didn't quite know what to do with this whole Cause thing. That first week I was at The Rock, the place was half-empty. Last week when I visited, it was almost full. I remember scanning the room and seeing there were tons of kids from Brentwood there. Eric had seemed overwhelmed, like he had no clue what to do with all of those noobie Christians. The group was definitely shaking things up. One of the Emo kids Nick invited to youth group was even hitting on the pastor's daughter (and I think she liked it!)

FIRESTARTER

So, the fire burned on. And it definitely was not a controlled burn.

But despite the havoc, or maybe because of it, eventually the movement gathered enough momentum that its buzz spilled over to the home front. My little brother, Zeke, who's a sophomore, told my dad about the growing phenomenon among my friends. So, I started getting crap from Dad about hanging out with extremists and about how I should stay focused on my running schedule and homework.

No problem when my parents caught my big brother smoking marijuana downstairs—he was just "sowing his wild oats." No, he was smoking his wild oats, but as long as he didn't endanger his full-ride scholarship to USC, no big deal. Me, however? I hang out too long with religious nut jobs and I'm the bad guy. Or maybe it's because I could only get a track scholarship to state and Dad is bitter.

Makes me think of the conversation Nick and I had at the Starbucks that triggered this whole thing to begin with, that day before Kailey became a Christian. Maybe there's something to the whole "heavenly dad" thing. I certainly can't stand my earthly one. I just wish that God was as real to me as he was to everyone else in "THE Cause." I want something real. Real relationships and a real mission, because the whole materialistic dream my Dad shoves at me of chasing the Almighty Dollar by going off to college and getting a good job and blah, blah, blah, seems fake to me. Especially now, in light of Matt's suicide.

Meanwhile, little dorky David's got a real mission. Hard to believe. Here I am feeling hollow as a drum when it comes to a life purpose, while that little nerd's gotten all excited about how he's now using Facebook to make friends and "P3" them (his term for "pray, pursue, persuade"). His strategy was to put the words "Ask me about THE Cause" in his "About Me" and on his status. Taking a cue from Jen, he would then ask his new friends all about them and their interests and they inevitably would ask him about THE Cause. Then he'd invite them to accept, in his words, "the message and mission of Jesus" as their very own.

I need something as my very own, something to give my life purpose and meaning. More than chasing my Dad's dreams. I'm actually a little jealous I guess—not of the message, but of these Christians' sense of mission.

THE Cause crew members have started spiritual discussion groups on campus where anybody interested in spirituality can come to talk. They pick a topic like "What's the purpose of life?" or "Why are there so many religions?" or "Who was Jesus and what was his message?" and then talk about it. I sat in once when Kailey led the "What is the purpose of life?" discussion. She asked the questions, listened to everybody's point of view and then shared what the Bible had to say about it, and ended by sharing the message of Jesus. It was an interesting discussion. It helped me to better understand what drives these Christians to share their faith so passionately and purposefully.

While I still think Christianity is a myth embraced by simpletons (yes, I just called all my best friends simpletons), I do appreciate their sincerity. I can see they're just trying to share the message of God in the most compelling way they can. Nobody's jumping on the cafeteria tables during lunch and screaming, "You all are on a highway to hell!!!" But they're not in a backroom of the school either, waiting for people to come to them. They're truly trying to find the "relational and relentless" balance and I respect them for it. They have something I want—no, not Jesus, but… purpose.

9

Kailey never gives up. She's one relentless girl. Even though her first effort at sharing Jesus with Emma exploded in her face like a grenade, she's back at it again. And she invited Nick, Jen and I along to join her. I knew it was a ploy to rope me into the Jesus cult, too, but Jen insisted that we join them. So there I was on a Friday night headed to Denny's for a late dinner/early breakfast with the expressed agenda of talking more about God.

After the five of us settled into a corner booth, Kailey wasted no time before launching the conversation in a spiritual direction. "Emma, I'm so sorry I offended you before with my attempt to talk to you about God. I didn't mean to make such a mess of it. Can you ever forgive me?"

"Yeah, I can. I did kinda over react myself," Emma volunteered.

"Ever since Matt's suicide, it feels like I just can't let the chance slip by to really talk to you about God. But it's only because I care about you as a friend, Emma," Kailey said with genuine emotion.

"I know, I feel so bad about Matt, too," Emma said softly. "Last time when I blew up at you, I guess you just pushed all the wrong buttons for me with your hellfire talk. You see, years ago when I was a little kid, my parents forced me to go to church every week. Then in middle school, I got to a place where I totally hated it. One week I was so frustrated I asked a bunch of questions about hell just to make my little old lady Sunday school teacher mad. Well, I succeeded, alright. I pushed her right over the top and she lit into me. I was so angry I vowed never to have anything to do with religion ever again no matter what my parents threatened me with."

"But Christianity isn't about religion, it's about a relationship," Kailey said, nodding toward Nick. "Nick's the one who first told me that. And I've found that it's so true! This may sound stupid, but I really like the idea of a God who loves me so much that he sent his own son to die for my sins so that I could spend eternity with him."

"And that's fine for you, but I believe that as long as you're a good person then you'll make it to heaven or come back to earth as a tree or a flower or whatever," Emma replied.

Kailey looked at Nick and smiled.

"What?" Emma asked, catching the glance.

Nick took over, "Emma, let me ask you a question. What if you're wrong?"

"What do you mean? There's no right or wrong when it comes to this sort of stuff," she shot back with a hint of defensiveness. A couple weeks ago I would have totally agreed with her, but now I wasn't quite so sure. I decided to keep my mouth shut for now.

FIRESTARTER

"Are you sure about that, Emma?" Nick asked.

She shrugged.

Kailey took over. "Well, if you think about it, there are right and wrong answers on the tests we take at school. There are laws of physics, there are facts of math, so why couldn't there be laws and facts in the spiritual realm?"

Emma responded, "Yeah, I guess that makes sense, but I just try to keep an open mind."

In a totally non-condescending way, Kailey put her hand on Emma's shoulder and shared, "Me too. But that's what led me to Jesus. When Nick explained to me how Jesus claimed to be God and the only way to God, it started making me think, 'Hey, am I open-minded enough to consider that God made me to have a relationship with Him, and Jesus may be the only way to restore that relationship and to get to heaven?'"

Emma responded, "So you're saying there's a real heaven—"

CHAPTER 9

"—and a real hell, if you believe Jesus' words," Kailey interrupted.

Emma continued, "Yeah, and that Jesus is the only way to heaven and, I guess, to escape hell— according to the Christian religion, er, relationship, or, ah—you know what I mean."

Nick jumped in, "Yes! And unlike other belief systems, Christianity is the only one that is received through trusting and not trying."

Blank stare from Emma as she slurped her shake.

"Let me explain," Nick leaned forward and continued. "Most religions say that to go to heaven or to the next life or to reincarnate as something better or whatever, that you need to be a good person, but the Bible says in Romans 3:23, 'For all have sinned and fall short of the glory of God.'"

"What does that mean? Isn't being good a good thing?" Emma looked confused.

Nick explained, "Sure it's a good thing. But it's not good enough to get us into heaven. When God says we all fall short, it means that we all sin, that we're selfish and self-centered and that we miss the mark of God's perfect standard."

"But I'm basically a good person. How can God expect perfection?" Emma challenged.

"Well, Jesus said in Matthew 5:48, 'Be perfect, therefore, as your heavenly Father is perfect.' And in Revelation 21:27, the Bible says this about heaven, 'Nothing impure will ever enter it, nor will anyone who does what is shameful or deceitful, but only those whose names are written in the Lamb's book of life.'" Nick continued, "So, to get into heaven you have to be as perfect as God, you could have never lied or done anything wrong and your name must be written in the Lamb's book of life."

"Whoa, this conversation is taking a turn into the totally bizarre," I interrupted. I was always uncomfortable with the whole God as the "big judge in the sky" talk. My mind was starting to drift off in the direction of my own perfectionist, disapproving

Dad, when Emma refocused my thoughts by giving voice to my sentiments exactly.

"Well, if perfection is the standard, then I guess we're all in deep, deep trouble," she said flatly.

"That's the whole point," Nick continued. "We're all in trouble because of our sins. We all mess up and miss the mark. As a result, we could never get into heaven because God is a perfect God and cannot stand the presence of sin.

"But," Jen jumped in unexpectedly, "although he hates our sin, he loves us desperately. He loves us so much that he sent his Son to die in our place and pay the penalty for all of our sins. Jesus himself said in John 3:16, 'For God so loved the world that he gave his one and only Son, that whoever believes in him shall not perish but have eternal life.'"

I looked at her, amazed that she was quoting the Bible. Ever since Matt's suicide, she'd become much more vocal and serious about all this Jesus stuff, no longer taking a backseat to Nick and Kailey's "relational and relentless" one-two punch.

FIRESTARTER

"So, if I just believe that Jesus existed and stuff, I'll be safe?" Emma interrupted.

"Yeah," Jen replied. "That's what makes it so cool. It's that easy." Then looking toward Nick she added, "Isn't it?"

"Well, this word 'believe' is more than just acknowledging someone existed," Nick explained. "And this is really important, this word means to trust in or rely upon someone fully. If I tell you that I'm going to pick you up at 8 o'clock tomorrow morning to take you to Disneyland and you believed me, then you would be waiting for me at 8 o'clock to pick you up. In other words, you would trust in my character enough to be ready and waiting at 8. In the same way, if you believe in Jesus to forgive you for all your sins and take you to heaven—"

"Why not Disneyland?" I interrupted, trying to lighten the mood.

"Who says there aren't rides in heaven?" Jen shot back. "Just not the 'It's a Small World After All' ride."

"Yeah, that would be hell," Emma interjected with a smirk. "So, what about good people who don't trust in Jesus?"

"Great question," Nick answered, "but remember, there are no good people. I mean if we compare ourselves with others, we may feel like we're better than someone else, but when we compare ourselves to God, we realize we're all just dirtbags. The Bible says everyone has sinned and everyone has fallen short of God's perfection."

"Losers," Emma said.

"Yeah," I responded, surprising even myself. "But wasn't it you, Kailey, who was telling us the other day about the basic storyline that every good play follows. What was it again?"

"Yes! No! But wait!" Kailey answered. "Those are the three phases of any good drama or movie. There's always the 'Yes!' moment. Something is going good. Like in *Grease*, it's the relationship with Danny and Sandra D over the summer when they fall in love."

FIRESTARTER

Jen took over, "And then there is the 'No!' moment when they break up or whatever because they are so different."

"And then the 'But wait!' moment when she dresses like a sleaze so that she can date him," Emma added.

"Hey!" Kailey yelled a little too loudly. Everyone at the table next to us stopped talking and stared.

"Well, if the pants fit…" Emma answered.

"Actually they didn't," Kailey responded, triggering a round of laughter.

When the snorts stopped, Nick steered the conversation back to the point. "When it comes to the gospel, the 'Yes!' moment is when God made Adam and Eve to be in perfect relationship with him. They had no sin or shame. Everything was good. The 'No!' moment was when they disobeyed the command of God and immediately became corrupted by sin. As a result, every baby ever born has come into this world kicking and screaming and wanting its own way. We see the result of our sin in the world all around us. There's war, famine, crime, abuse, lying, stealing, cheating and all that crap because of the 'No!' moment in this human history drama."

"Stuff like the Holocaust and mankind destroying the environment," Jen interjected.

"Sure. Anything and everything in this world that is a result of the selfishness of humanity can be traced back to that 'No!' moment when humans first turned their backs on God and said, 'I want it my way!' in the Garden of Eden," Nick continued.

"So is Jesus the 'But wait!' part?" Emma asked, intrigued.

"Exactly!" Kailey and Nick said in unison.

"When He died on the cross, He was dying in our place for our sins—all the ways we've fallen short. It's not hard for any of us to call to mind our selfishness and all the ways we've missed the mark of God's perfection. Holy, perfect God. Unholy, imperfect man. Something had to give or our sins would keep us separated from God in this life and condemn us to hell in the next. But Jesus paid the price for our sins. He died so that you and I could be reconnected in relationship with God and someday go to heaven." Nick was moving into preacher mode.

"So, what you're saying is that if I believe in Jesus, trust in him, then all my sins are forgiven and I'll go to heaven someday?" Emma asked.

"Yeah," Nick answered. "But it's not just all about 'someday,' it's also about 'today.'"

Kailey interrupted, unable to contain herself, "Okay, so, let's say you had cancer and somehow discovered the cure to cancer. Say you took it yourself and you were cured. Would you share that cure with me if I had cancer?"

"Duh!" Emma replied.

"Okay, so, in a sense, you'd be saying 'Hey, I tried this cure and it works. You should try it too!' Right?" Kailey continued, "In the same way, all of us have the 'cancer' of sin and are headed toward something worse than death."

CHAPTER 9

"The eternal 'It's a Small World After All' ride from hell," Jen interrupted.

"Exactly!" Kailey said with a smile. "And that cure that saves us from hell also gives us a purpose here and now."

"To keep people out of hell," Emma said.

"Exactly," Kailey responded. "But it's not just the hell that they are headed to after they die, it's also the hell that many of them are living in right now. Like Matt Cromby. He must have been going through hell and none of us ever knew it."

"And what I'm just starting to realize," Jen added quietly, "is that Jesus not only died for my sins so that I could be in heaven someday, but that He gave me a purpose right now. To tell others about his offer to rescue them from sin and its consequences, the hell they're going to and going through."

"That's a pretty good 'But wait!' if it's true," Emma acknowledged.

FIRESTARTER

"What do you think, Jared?" Jen asked turning to look directly into my eyes.

"Sure it is...if it's true. But it's a pretty big 'if,' if you ask me," I responded.

"Well, I believe it, Emma," Kailey said with utter conviction. "I don't have all the facts and stuff like Nick or his youth pastor, but I know that until a couple weeks ago I had a longing deep within me that was finally satisfied when I finally trusted Jesus."

"Bring her a Venti Jesus, please!" I cracked.

Emma threw me a confused look before she said, "I don't know, this is a lot of stuff to process."

"So, Emma," Nick interjected, "say over the next few weeks, you read the book of John, like Jared is doing. Then we can all process together."

"Sounds like a plan," Emma responded. "After all, I refuse to become a Christian at a Denny's out of principle."

10

Week four into our little social experiment, the blaze hit home and erupted into a firestorm. I was mad. I had every right to be.

Zeke, my little brother, came home and declared to our whole family that he'd become a Christian. This from the little snitch who'd gotten Dad on my case because I was hanging with extremists. My family was speechless at first and then enraged. I come from a long line of atheists who pride themselves on their open-minded, rational views.

FIRESTARTER

When Zeke explained that Emma had led him to Christ, I got really mad. I was more than mad, I was furious. I'd been part of the conversation that led Emma down the road to becoming a Christian.

Obviously Emma had become one of those "disciples" Nick was talking about. And obviously she had set her sights on Zeke and had bagged him.

Agggh! I feel like I've played a part in creating an unstoppable monster. This has gotten way too personal now with Zeke sucked in. I wish I'd done all I could to squash THE Cause. Stupid me, thinking this would be just an entertaining little side show as high school wound down.

My Dad interrupted my thoughts and vented his anger in my direction. "This is all your fault," he yelled. "You and that little group of Christian extremists you hang out with. What did you do, egg them on to brainwash your brother with all this Jesus nonsense?"

"Shut up, you jerk!" I yelled back as I bolted for the door and headed to my car. I got a wicked pleasure out of leaving rubber all over the driveway as I peeled out. I was supposed to meet Kailey at Starbucks anyway in ten minutes. She wanted to talk to me about something. Well, I wanted to talk to her about something too. I couldn't wait for the confrontation, or should I say "intervention."

Enough was enough. Kailey was certainly going to get a piece of my mind. She was so compulsive about this Jesus stuff—compulsive about a lot of stuff in her life, actually. Almost like she was always running from something. Well, she'd be running from me soon, after I scorched her. Because now it was personal. And no matter what, Zeke was not going to be recruited into THE Cause crew. I was putting an end to that prospect right now.

———————

As I screeched into the parking lot I had my speech ready to go. Kailey was already there, sitting at our favorite table. Without stopping to order a drink, I stormed over to her and thundered down into my chair.

"What's the matter?" she asked.

FIRESTARTER

"You're the matter!" I said so loudly that half the place turned to look at me. Lowering my tone and glaring aggressively at her I said, "Are you happy now, now that my little brother has converted to your cult? Is he one of your little salvation trophies you can't wait to show off in youth group?"

"No, it's not like that," Kailey responded quietly. But I wasn't finished.

"What is it with all of you Christians who think you have to make everyone else Christians? To be honest, I liked you the way you were before you converted to Christianity, Kailey. At least you knew how to party! The only thing you know how to do now is preach!"

She tried to interrupt me but I was on a roll, "Now you've got everything turned upside down at Brentwood. It's 'Jesus this' and 'Jesus that' everywhere I turn. Now you've got a group of 75 cult members meeting every day at lunchtime, praying and planning and bragging about all their new converts! And I can't believe that I thought it was fun to watch this little religion experiment.

"But now my little brother's in the cult and I know Zeke. He's as stubborn as me. When he says he's in, he's in! Do you know what that means for me? My life is going to turn into a living hell with my Dad! He already blames me for Zeke's indoctrination and it's going to get worse as the reality sinks in. The jerk is already on my case about every little thing and you and Emma just gave him more ammunition. Thanks, Kailey. Thanks a lot! Some friend you are."

Quietly Kailey put her hand on mine and said, "I'm sorry, Jared. Making your life hell was never my intent. My intent was…."

I cut her off, "I don't care what your intent was, Kailey. Here's what I care about, here's what I want to know. Why are you so obsessed with this Jesus stuff? What are you running from? Is this God stuff some sort of crutch for you? Did you have a near death experience or something? Or do something horrible in your past that you're running from?"

I could see tears welling in her eyes. But I couldn't stop.

FIRESTARTER

"Why are you so manic? You are OCD! You have an obsession with this thing. It's time to GET A LIFE!" I yelled, pounding my fist on the table so hard that her drink spilled.

With tears running down her face, she ran out to her car like the sprinter she was...and she drove away...she ran away. As I borrowed a rag from the barista to clean up the spill, I tried to feel regret, but I didn't. I was still furious.

at Starbucks and she left in tears. She should never have been driving. She was a mess, man."

Nick was staring at me speechless when the officer who wanted to see me walked up to us and asked Nick, "Is this Jared?"

Nick just nodded.

"This is all my fault," I sobbed again. "She was upset because we'd just had a fight."

"Son, look at me," the officer said kindly. "This wasn't your fault. She was T-boned by a drunk driver at the stoplight."

"What?" I asked, trying to decipher his meaning.

"She was hit by a drunk driver who ran a stoplight. It wasn't her fault and it wasn't your fault. It was the drunk driver's fault." After giving me a moment to absorb this thought, he continued on, "Son, I was the first one on the scene after the accident. She was still alive, but barely. She was losing a lot of blood. I was trying to get her out of the car but when it became obvious that I couldn't, she put her hand on mine and she whispered the words, 'Tell Jared that I'm praying for him.' And then she died right there."

Her words, though filtered through this cop, still hit me like a shot to my solar plexus. At the moment of her death, she was thinking about me. She was praying for me. After how badly I had treated her, she showed me what Jesus was like, still thinking about others instead of herself.

I collapsed and wept again and I didn't stop crying for a long time.

When I regained my sense of presence, I was at Kailey's house. Jen was sitting next to me holding my hand. Kailey's family was in the kitchen hugging and holding and crying. Family and friends milled around.

"Look out the window," Jen whispered. As I did, I was shocked. Hundreds of teenagers huddled on the front lawn most of them kneeling and praying. David, that little dork who somehow found a way to endear himself to me and everyone he befriended, was leading them all in prayers for the family.

CHAPTER 11

I'll never forget when Kailey's Mom, that shallow shell of a woman, walked up to me and said with surprising sincerity, "You were her best friend, Jared. I want you to do the eulogy at her funeral."

She handed me her journal and said, "This may help you as you prepare for what to say. I haven't read it. I don't think she would want me to. But I'm pretty sure that she would want you to."

"I'd be honored," I stammered.

Later that night, I went home and read her journal from beginning to end, knowing that at last, I would find out what she had been running from that pushed her to Jesus.

12

It took me two hours to read through most of Kailey's journal. I was going to wait to write the eulogy until I'd read her last journal entry. One hundred of the one hundred and fifty pages of her journal were filled with her deepest thoughts, dreams and hurts. The other fifty, waiting to be filled, were cut short by tragedy.

Besides not getting along with her Mom and not having a Dad at home, she lived a surprisingly normal life. How could that be? As I scoured the pages of her journal, I saw no deep dark secret. What I did see was longing. On every page she was searching for something, for anything that would satisfy for the long haul. Hers was a restless soul until she met Jesus and found the passion fuel she needed to channel her energy and set her ablaze for God.

What spilled out of the pages of her journal was her dissatisfaction with track, and then with drama. But never with Jesus. As I read how she talked about him and sharing his message, I felt like I was overhearing a one-sided transcript between two lovers. She longed for him and she found what she was longing for in him.

How can that be? How could she find hope in a man she never met, a man who lived 2,000 years ago and claimed to be God? Could he really be who she thought he was?

I reached for the book of John Nick had given me a month or so ago and flipped the pages. I'd gone through the motions of reading it over the past weeks, only because I'd promised Nick I would. But this time, I decided to read it to look for clues to help me understand Kailey's life.

There in the late night hours, I read and read and read. This time Kailey's love for her Lord gave me different eyes.

I could feel the atheist inside resisting what I now knew to be true. This was no ordinary man. This was no ordinary book. Jesus was too real, too loving, too pure, too compassionate to be fake. Nick had given me every argument known to man to try to convince me that Jesus was real. But Kailey's passion for Jesus finally brought me to a decision point. I especially loved the verse in John chapter 20, verse 31, "But these are written that you may believe that Jesus is the Christ, the Son of God, and that by believing you may have life in his name."

The word "you" really got to me. It's almost like I could put my own name in there, "But these are written that you, Jared, may believe that Jesus is the Christ, the Son of God, and that by believing you, Jared, may have life in his name."

This book feels all too personal to be a forgery or fake, like my Dad says. There is something powerful in it. There is something authentic about it. And as I think about the accident, I can't help but wonder… if this whole Christianity thing is true, then Kailey is as happy as she has ever been. She is with Jesus, the one whom she loved, the one who loved her.

The one who loves me.

Dropping to my knees, it felt like God was right there in the room with me. So, I prayed out loud, "Dear God, I don't know how to do this right. But I've been around enough real Christians to know that when I pray, all I have to do is to talk to you from the heart." Tears started to stream down my face as I continued, "God, I'm a screw up. I'm a sinner. I'm an atheist. Or, at least I was. But now I do believe…" I started weeping more and cried out louder, "I do believe that Jesus died for my sins. I believe that you love me. I believe! I BELIEVE! I BELIEVE! God, tell Kailey, please tell Kailey that her prayers have been answered."

My prayer was interrupted by pounding on my door. I was sure it was my Dad, ready to scathe away. As I whipped open the door, refusing to wipe away my tears, I was shocked to see my little brother standing there weeping, too. He had heard my prayer. We embraced and wept tears of joy and grief mingled together.

Then my thoughts turned to Jen and Nick. I couldn't wait to tell them, too.

All for one, and one for all.

13

The morning of Kailey's funeral service, I was nervous. The church was packed. I was led by an usher to a back room where Eric and the soloist were seated. Eric was officiating the service. Kailey's Mom had asked him to.

He asked me how I was doing. I told him fine.

"Would you mind if I prayed before we go out on stage?" he asked.

"You can pray for us," I said quietly.

FIRESTARTER

He looked surprised by my openness to prayer; so, I told him what had happened to me the night Kailey died.

He teared up as I shared, nodded and just started praying from the heart.

As we walked out on stage, me wearing one of my big brother's suits that felt a little big in the shoulders, I was overwhelmed. The church was packed. Half the school had to be there. People lined the back and overflowed into the lobby.

After an opening song, a prayer and reading from the Bible by the main pastor of the church, Eric got up to deliver the sermon. He talked about Kailey's remarkable passion for God. He described her as a firestarter who had sparked an unstoppable blaze with her passion for Jesus and his message of grace. He shared how her passion to share the gospel at first repelled him, then convicted him and finally transformed him. He explained how the last four weeks had totally changed his view of youth ministry.

He talked about how he no longer viewed outreach as a result of discipleship but as a trigger to discipleship. Although I didn't understand everything he was saying, I did understand that he was getting refocused on what matters most: not meetings but mission.

Eric finished by sharing the gospel. Kailey would have wanted it that way. He finished his sermon with the words, "If Kailey is watching from heaven, I'm sure she's cheering for every single one of you to believe in the Savior who gave her so much hope."

He had the audience bow their heads and close their eyes and told the crowd, "If you are willing to trust in Jesus as your Savior right now, would you please raise your hand?"

I gasped at the many hands that were raised. Granted, she must have singlehandedly led twenty or thirty people into a relationship with God during her short time as a Christian, but now there were hundreds and hundreds who responded.

Eric closed his prayer and then introduced me to do the eulogy. My hands were sweaty and I felt a little dizzy as I made my way toward the podium. Eric smiled at me and put his hand on my shoulder as we passed each other. It felt as though I were walking in slow motion up to my spot on stage, like one of those dreams where you are trying to run from something but are slowed down by some kind of mud or quicksand.

Looking out at the sea of faces touched by Kailey's life and death, individuals came into focus— students, teachers, parents.

I tensed as my gaze fell on my parents and brother seated by the side aisle, my Dad with that snide look that seemed to be permanently pasted on. He wasn't going to be happy with the message I was about to share. What an ego hit to raise two sons in such an "intellectually stimulating" environment, and then find both of them gullible enough to buy into this Jesus stuff. My brother's eyes shone with tears, but encouragement radiated from his face.

I saw Kailey's Mom sitting in the front row, her tears driving her mascara down her cheeks. Nick and Jen were in the front row too. Nick threw me the thumbs up sign, which pulled my thoughts back to a happier day when Kailey nailed it in *Grease*. Little did we know that would be the closest she'd ever get to Broadway.

I sent up a silent "Help me!" prayer to God as I carefully placed my spiral notebook and Kailey's journal on the slightly inclined wood of the podium.

Swallowing hard, I began.

"Wow. There sure are a lot of people here this morning. I think I just peed my pants a little on the way up here. I'm glad this podium is big enough to cover me up."

The laughter from the crowd broke the tension in the room and my heart.

"My name is Jared Hildebrand and I am Kailey's friend. I use the word 'am' because I believe Kailey is more alive than ever…in heaven. That may shock some of you who know me. I've always prided myself as being an intellectual who sees the world through the lenses of the rationalist.

FIRESTARTER

"But Kailey changed all of that just a few days ago. She didn't live to see it, but if she is leaning over the banister of heaven now, I'm sure she's applauding, not just because I, the infamous atheist from Brentwood High, became a follower of Jesus, but because so many more of you did today. Kailey's reached even more people in her death than she did in her life. Eric said in his talk that the angels rejoice over one sinner who repents. I'm sure that if they're rejoicing, then Kailey's up there partying, too." My voice broke with emotion.

Pausing to look down at my notes, I took a deep breath and continued. "Kailey was a mystery to me. She always seemed like she was running from something. I had imagined some emotional scar that had torn her so deeply that she had to keep running. She was just too intense, too focused. She was running away and it showed.

"I was convinced that it was some deep pain she was running from that drove her to excel at everything. She was a championship runner. But she didn't know how to pace herself. She'd sprint a marathon if she could. She ran so hard and so fast that she got injured and couldn't race anymore…on the track anyway.

"She sprinted in her studies. She sprinted at drama. She sprinted at life. And when she became a Christian, she ran like there was no tomorrow.

"Our last encounter was not a pretty one. For the first time in a long time, we got in an argument and she left crying. A half hour later, I got the call from Nick that she had died. I rushed to the scene. That's when the police officer told me her dying words, 'Tell Jared I'm praying for him.'"

I could hear the sniffles from the audience begin. I could feel the tears start to well in my own eyes. And my voice started to crack as I continued, "At first I thought her wreck was my fault, but I found out that she was killed by a drunk driver. Even then, the first thought on her mind was of me and my salvation.

"When Kailey's Mom asked me to do this eulogy, she gave me Kailey's journal. I was expecting to find out what she was running from. I came up empty. She actually had a pretty normal life. Sure she didn't have her Dad around and her and her Mom had some conflicts, but that's normal."

Kailey's Mom nodded at me.

"As I scoured her journal, I couldn't find any evidence of some traumatic event. But what I did find was thirst and hunger and longing. She wasn't running from something, she was running toward something. It was evident that she had found that something in the message and mission of Jesus. She embraced Christianity, not as a religion but as a cause, THE Cause. In Jesus, she had found what she had been hoping for and running toward. She was determined to take as many people as she could with her on this journey to heaven. She knew that every second at least one person somewhere on the planet dies. She knew that many of those people would end up in hell unless someone told them about Jesus.

"Matt's suicide added even more urgency to her reality that the next one to die could be you or could be me," my eyes welled up with tears, so I paused to pull myself together. "But it wasn't us who died. It was her.

"Now it's up to us to finish the race that she started. I want to talk to the Christian teenagers in this room who go to Brentwood. Let's finish the race. Let's accomplish THE Cause together. What is it? It's not a meeting to attend, but a mission to accomplish. It's not a program, but an idea. The idea that you and I are the outreach meeting, that you and I have a cause, THE Cause to accomplish. Let's love everyone with the love of Jesus, the same brand of love that we saw in Kailey. Let's serve other teenagers humbly and listen deeply to their hopes and hurts."

Feeling a rush of emotion, I raised my voice. "Because if it's true, if this gospel we believe is true, then the story of Jesus is the ultimate love story and the ultimate challenge. We must rescue our friends, our neighbors, our families from the hell they're headed to and the hell they must be going through.

"We must, we must, we MUST finish what God used Kailey to start. Look at the blaze she started in just thirty days of talking to her friends about Jesus and mobilizing them to do the same with their friends. Like Eric said, she was the firestarter who took four teenagers and an atheist at lunch time and ignited the fire into an unstoppable force. And now the fire is burning brightly, fueled by our determination to talk to our friends about Jesus."

"Look at all Kailey accomplished in thirty days. If this is what she accomplished almost singlehandedly, what could all of us do together if we embraced THE Cause? Seniors, we have thirty days until the last day of school. Let's set our world ablaze and talk to as many as we can about Jesus, and then let's take THE Cause to our colleges and workplaces after that. Underclassmen, you'll have to carry THE Cause after we're gone. But be forewarned, it's gonna be hard work and take lots of prayer because, in the words of Kailey in her journal, 'There's no way I can do this without the strength of Jesus and the power of the Holy Spirit.'"

After pausing to take a drink from the cup of water on a shelf under the pulpit, with the excitement palpable in the auditorium, I continued, "And to those in this room who don't know Jesus, gird yourself. I don't want to scare you, but I do need to let you know that we are going to pray for you, pursue you and do our best to persuade you to accept the message and mission of Jesus. We don't want to coerce you to convert, but we do want to paint a picture of Christianity with our lives and with our lips that's so compelling you cannot resist."

The crowd erupted. This was Kailey's final standing ovation.

After twenty seconds or so of thunderous applause, the crowd sat back down. I could see from the two empty seats off the side aisle that my Mom and Dad had used this as an opportunity to make their escape. My own lightning strike was going to happen in an about an hour or two when I got home. But my brother was still standing there beaming with joy.

"In closing, I thought I would read from Kailey's journal. This was her last journal entry, written Friday afternoon,

Dear God,

I'm headed to Starbucks to meet with Jared and I ask for your strength. He's been in so many conversations about you these past weeks. And just when I think that the wall of

disbelief he's constructed is about to break, he adds another brick back in.

Lord, I'm afraid. He's much smarter than me and he knows his stuff. If Nick couldn't convince him to become a Christian, then I know that I can't. But you can. I ask that you send your Holy Spirit to convict him and convince him. I ask that you use me as your vessel today.

I thank you, God, for all that you've done in the last thirty days. Tons of teenagers have come to Christ! Teenagers are talking to teenagers who are talking to more teenagers. I heard that even Jared's brother, Zeke, trusted in Jesus today! You get all of the glory for what has taken place!

And I see you sparking something at Brentwood. More teens are involved and it's much messier. It feels raw, authentic, viral and divine all at the same time. Spread this messiness to other schools and teenagers across this city, state, nation and world! God, unleash revival.

Use me to help spark it, God. Use me. I only have thirty days left at Brentwood before I graduate. Use me to spark revival here through THE Cause. Then use me at college to do the same thing. Use me for the rest of my life to live THE Cause and call others to do the same.

At the end of my life, may I be able to look back and say with the apostle Paul,

> *For I am already being poured out like a drink offering, and the time has come for my departure. I have fought the good fight, I have finished the race, I have kept the faith.*

> *2 Timothy 4:7*

I pray these things in Jesus' Name,

Amen."

Looking up toward heaven I said, "Kailey, you were our firestarter. God used you to spark the fire that's blazing around us. And now you've fought the

FIRESTARTER

good fight. You've finished the race. You've kept the faith. May we do the same.

"Thirty days and counting."

The crowd fell silent as I picked up my spiral and Kailey's journal and walked away with a steely determination in my eyes.

THE
~~the~~ Cause

Did you know that every second at least one person on this planet dies and faces their eternal destiny?

You have the message of hope and life others need. No matter how scared you may be or intimidated you may feel, the Holy Spirit wants to use you to be the firestarter who spreads the gospel to all your friends.

Although there are many causes you can get involved with, many of which are good and beneficial to the world, there is only one cause that will change lives both now and forever...THE Cause.

THE Cause is all about making disciples who make disciples, based on Jesus' command in Matthew 28:19 to "go and make disciples of all nations...." It's about taking the gospel from where you're at, to where they're at, in a relational and relentless way. It's about equipping those who say yes to Jesus, to get others to say yes, as well.

Every teen deserves to hear the Good News of God's grace and love from another teen they know and trust. By launching THE Cause at your school, you can play a key role in reaching your generation with the transforming message of Jesus.

THE
the Cause

There are 67,342 public and private high schools and middle schools in America alone. Be part of something bigger than yourself. Join THE Cause and change your world, starting with your own school!

If you're interested in being part of this movement to ignite every school with the message and mission of Jesus, go to **dare2share.org/thecause** to learn more.

THE
~~the~~ Cause

THE Cause Circle

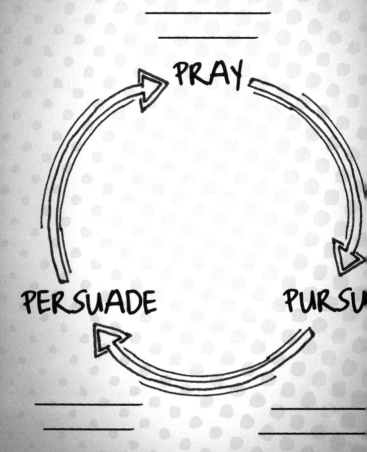

About the **Authors**

Greg Stier is President of Dare 2 Share Ministries (D2S) and has impacted the lives of hundreds of thousands of teenagers across the United States through D2S training conferences. Dare 2 Share's mission is to mobilize teenagers to relationally and relentlessly reach their generation for Christ. Greg has written numerous books to help teens relationally and relentlessly share their faith, including *Venti Jesus Please* and *Dare 2 Share: A Field Guide to Sharing Your Faith.* He lives in Arvada, Colorado, with his wife Debbie, and children, Jeremy and Kailey.

Jane Dratz serves as a writer and editor for Dare 2 Share Ministries. She has written numerous articles that challenge, equip and mobilize teenagers for evangelistic action. Jane and her husband Steve live in Wheat Ridge, Colorado. They have successfully navigated their three children, Andrea, Chris and Elizabeth through their teen years and into adulthood.

Want to Become a Firestarter?

Take the first steps in sharing Jesus with your friends using *Venti Jesus Please*, the prequel to *Firestarter*!

Venti Jesus Please captures a candid conversation between Jared, Jen and Nick at their local Starbucks as they dialogue about life, God, truth and relationship.

Designed to be given away to your friends who don't know Jesus, *Venti Jesus Please* explains the compelling gospel message clearly and concisely.

Use this book to bring up God with your friends!

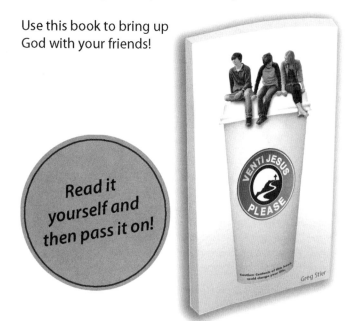

Read it yourself and then pass it on!

Learn more or buy your copy at dare2share.org.